Today earth scientists seem to be on the verge of answering some of the most basic questions about the earth, of understanding why the earth has continents and mountains, volcanoes and earthquakes. They are on the verge of understanding the forces that shape and change the earth, that keep it alive within, and that make it a planet where many kinds of life are possible.

In THIS RESTLESS EARTH Patricia Lauber describes recent theories about the earth and the evidence on which they are based. Her clear and dramatic presentation makes this book a stimulating introduction to modern geophysics.

Cover photograph: View into a lava tunnel on the new island of Surtsey.

This Restless Earth

This Restless Earth

by Patricia Lauber
illustrated by John Polgreen

RANDOM HOUSE SCIENCE LIBRARY
RANDOM HOUSE · NEW YORK

For helpful suggestions in the preparation of this book, the author and publisher are grateful to Dr. Charles Drake of the Lamont-Doherty Geological Observatory.

The photographs in this book are reproduced through the courtesy of: Alaska Pictorial Service: 22, 27, 78 (top), 115 (bottom); American Museum of Natural History: 56, 78 (margin); Camera Hawaii: Werner Stoy—66 (top); Consulate General of Iceland: 217; Culver Pictures: 41; De Wys, Inc.: Martin Vanderwall—77 (bottom); Editorial Photocolor Archives, Inc.: 18; Fundamental Photographs: 30, 98; Library of Congress: 57; Lick Observatory: 8; Monkmeyer Press Photo Service: 59, 62, 66 (bottom), Feily—58 (both), Pro Pix —115 (top); NASA: 13, 42, 108, 123; Tad Nichols: 46, 47; Photo Researchers: John Lewis Stage—67 (bottom); Solarfilma: 2, 5, 61; from *Surtsey: The New Island in the North Atlantic* by Sigurdur Thorarinsson. All rights reserved. Reprinted by permission of The Viking Press, Inc.: Cover, 3; Swiss National Tourist Office: 77 (top); Teledyne Exploration Company: 82; United Press International: 21; United States Geological Survey Photo: 43 (both).

The map on page 105 was made available through the courtesy of: Dr. F. J. Vine. It has been reprinted by: *Sea Frontiers* and *The Geological Society of America.*

Contents

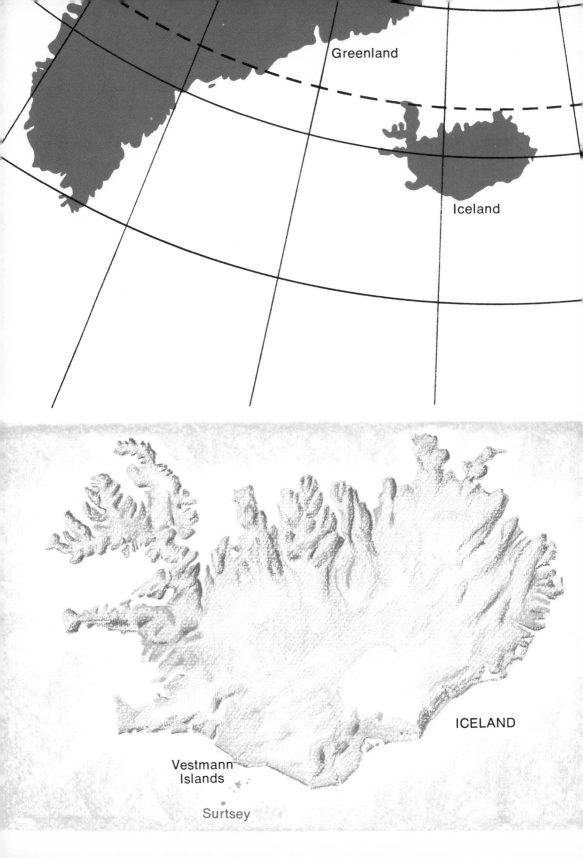

Greenland

Iceland

Vestmann
Islands

Surtsey

ICELAND

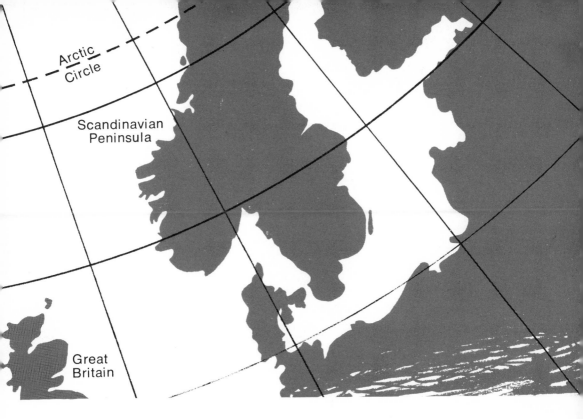

Arctic
Circle

Scandinavian
Peninsula

Great
Britain

1   An Island Is Born

In mid-November of 1963 an island was born in the
North Atlantic, some 20 miles off the southwestern
coast of Iceland. It had given only one sign of its
coming. For three days farmers on the neighboring
Vestmann Islands had noticed a bad smell in the air.
It was a sulfurous smell, like the odor of rotten eggs,
and the farmers could not discover where it was
coming from.

Early in the morning of November 14, the crew of
an Icelandic fishing vessel noticed the same smell.
The engineer thought that it might have something to
do with the ship, but he could find nothing wrong.
About 7:15 the cook, who was on watch, saw some-

Surtsey on November 18, 1963, the fifth day of the eruption

thing rise out of the sea to the southeast. At first, in the dim light of dawn, he could not make out what it was. Then he realized it was smoke. Thinking that a ship was on fire, he went below and woke the captain. Through his binoculars the captain saw black columns erupting from the sea. He suspected that he was seeing not a burning ship but a volcano rising from the ocean. The hours that followed proved him right. He was watching the volcanic eruption that built the island later named Surtsey.

Some days earlier a volcano had started to erupt 425 feet below the surface of the sea. It poured out gases and volcanic ash and cinder. The gases, bubbling to the surface, accounted for the sulfurous smell in the air. The ash and cinder began to build a mountain. By the morning of November 15 the top

2

Aerial view on November 30, 1963. Surtsey was already 2,600 feet long.

of the volcano was 33 feet above the water and still growing rapidly. Columns of smoke and gases rose two miles into the air. Explosions blew out tremendous quantities of ash, cinder, and pumice. These materials rained down and built a cone that within six weeks rose 500 feet above sea level.

Violent eruptions continued through the winter. The sea steamed. Lightning flashed and crackled in the rising column of electrically charged ash, while the claps of thunder could be heard for miles. Whirlwinds formed in the hot, rising gases. Winter storms and heavy seas attacked the new island, sweeping away parts of it and changing its shape. At times it seemed as if the sea must win and the island disappear. But eruptions continued and material piled up faster than the sea could wash it away.

3

In April 1964, the violent eruptions stopped and lava began to flow. Red-hot lava flows covered the ash and cinder and cooled into a tough, hard surface. Lava reaching the sea hardened into a collar that surrounded the island and protected the beach and cliffs. Surtsey, it seemed, had come to stay. By summer the island covered nearly a square mile of area and its peak was more than 500 feet tall. These first lava flows stopped in May 1965, but new flows have since added to the island.

Surtsey had risen from the sea barren of life. Yet life of one kind or another soon appeared on the island. First to arrive were the seagulls. Surtsey was only two weeks old when observers saw seagulls lighting on it between explosive eruptions. In May 1964, a biologist began to look for life on the island. He found large numbers of microbes in the air above it. By summer, although the lava flows were continuing, there were butterflies and flies on Surtsey. Migratory birds had started to rest on the island in spring. Seals came ashore on the beaches. By the summer of 1965 kittiwakes were nesting on lava cliffs built only six months earlier.

Seeds of coastal plants such as sea rocket, lyme grass, and angelica drifted to the island shores, as did some living plants. By early June of 1965 sea rockets were growing on Surtsey. They had struck root in a place where they were sheltered by seaweed that had washed ashore. These first "settlers" were soon buried under volcanic ash and dust. But later new plants took their place, giving promise of the day when the bare black and gray rock of the island would wear the green colors of plant life.

Lava flows out of the crater and down to the sea in April 1964. Where lava met the sea, water turned to steam, lava cooled and hardened into a collar that kept Surtsey from being washed away.

To earth scientists and to biologists Surtsey was endlessly fascinating. It offered a chance to study a new volcano, to see new land take shape, to watch life win a foothold on barren rock. Earth scientists hoped that by studying what was happening to Surtsey they would gain a better understanding of the forces behind its growth, for in one sense Surtsey was not a surprise.

Surtsey rose from a huge underwater mountain range that runs down the middle of the Atlantic Ocean and is called the Mid-Atlantic Ridge. The ridge is the center of many earthquakes, and it is highly volcanic. Here and there its volcanic action has built mountains that thrust through the surface of the ocean, creating small islands such as Surtsey. Long ago vast outpourings of lava from the ridge built the big island of Iceland.

The ridge, however, is much more than a builder of islands. It is a sign of mighty forces at work within the earth. Many earth scientists are certain that these same forces are builders of continents and mountains and are the cause of earthquakes and volcanic eruptions. They see the ridge as a key to understanding the most basic secrets of the earth. Powered by the great heat energy within the earth, these forces helped to shape our planet when it was young, to give it land and sea and air, and so to make it the kind of planet where life could develop. The same forces have helped to keep the earth both a planet of life and a planet that is hospitable to many forms of life. They have made the earth the one very special planet among the nine that orbit our sun.

6

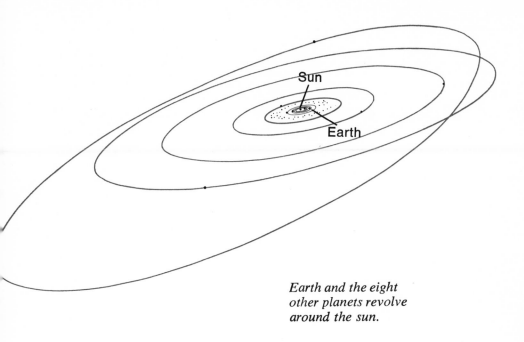

Sun

Earth

Earth and the eight other planets revolve around the sun.

2   A Planet of Life

The earth belongs to a family of planets that whirl through space, orbiting the star we call our sun. The planets are captives of the sun. They are held in orbit by the gravitational attraction between them and the sun, and so the sun and its planets form a unit in space. They are the main members of the solar system.

The solar system is often spoken of as a family because its members seem to be related. In fact, many scientists think that the sun and its planets came into being at the same time and in the same

7

way. They think, although they cannot be sure, that the sun and planets were born of a great cloud of gas and dust.

These scientists suppose that about 5 billion years ago a vast cloud of gas and dust was floating in space. The tiny particles that composed the cloud were spread very thin, and the cloud probably measured trillions of miles in diameter.

The particles were moving a little, and they tended to attract one another. Drifting slowly over huge distances, the particles swirled in toward the center of the cloud. The cloud began to contract. As it shrank and became denser, the force of gravity at its center grew stronger and stronger. Material swirled inward, slowly at first, then faster and faster giving the cloud a whirling motion. Eventually the cloud collapsed in on itself. It formed a huge, slowly spinning ball of gas and dust.

The spinning flattened the ball into a great disk. The disk was thickest at the middle, and there the particles of gas and dust were under tremendous pressure. Temperatures rose until this central part became white-hot and began to generate light and heat. In time it became our star, the sun.

While the sun was forming, the outer parts of the disk had broken up into whirlpools of gas and dust.

The dust particles settled toward the centers of the whirlpools. They began to collide. When two particles of the same size collided, they evaporated in the heat of the collision. When two particles of different sizes collided, the smaller one was added to the mass of the larger. The collisions went on for

The Great Nebula in Orion, a 180-trillion-mile-wide cloud of gas and dust

As larger masses swept up smaller ones, the largest masses became the planets.

hundreds of millions of years, with larger masses sweeping up smaller ones. Growing and growing, the largest masses became the planets. Each was wrapped in a thick atmosphere of gases.

Perhaps in the beginning all the newly formed planets were much alike. But it is clear that one, the third planet out from the sun, either was somehow different or became different. This was the earth, which developed into a planet of life.

No one can say for sure what the young earth was like, but many scientists think that radiation from the sun must have blasted away the lighter gases of the earth's first atmosphere. They think, too, that the young earth was probably very hot and growing hotter. It was still sweeping up matter from space, and the collisions added heat to it. As matter packed itself around the central core, pressure grew so great that heat was generated. The earth may have grown so hot that all its solid matter turned to gas.

10

After a while, the earth began to cool, giving off heat into space. The gases condensed into molten matter, and the earth became a mass of seething lava. At this time, scientists think, the earth's core formed. The heavier elements—iron and nickel—flowed toward the center of the earth, forming the dense core that the earth still has. Lighter materials rose toward the surface.

The earth went on cooling. For hundreds of millions of years the surface churned and bubbled, giving off gases. Then a thin, solid crust formed at the surface of the young earth. Underneath this crust the earth was still very hot. Molten rock erupted through cracks in the crust, bringing clouds of steam and gas to the surface. The steam and gas rose into the atmosphere and were held there by the earth's gravity.

Sometime during this early stage the air temperature dropped to a point where rain occurred. It was rain that fell only in the sky. When raindrops neared the earth's cooling but still hot crust, they evaporated. Steam rose into the atmosphere, condensed, and turned again to rain. Only when the crust cooled still more did the first rains strike the earth's surface. Over a long period of time, rain fell in a steady deluge. The wrinkled areas in the crust filled with water, and so the first oceans formed.

By the time it was 3 billion years old, the earth had a cool, solid crust. Much of the crust was probably covered by oceans. Land areas, if there were any, consisted of rock, perhaps with a little soil made of ground-up rock. The oceans and rocks were barren and lifeless. But the stage was now set for life.

Scientists do not know—and may never know—exactly how life began. But they think that heat and lightning acted on certain gases in the atmosphere, forming amino acids, which are the building blocks of living matter. Raindrops carried the amino acids into the sea. There, by ways and means unknown, a piece of living protein was produced. It split in two, and the two also divided. The dividing continued. The great chain of life had been established.

Much later the first plants evolved in the sea. And plants began to change the atmosphere. Like modern plants, the early ones took in carbon dioxide, which is a compound of carbon and oxygen, used the carbon, and released oxygen. Eventually the oxygen passed from the water to the atmosphere. Over many, many years the amount of free oxygen in the air increased greatly. And oxygen is chemically very active. It attacked and changed other gases in the air. In time the atmosphere became what it is today: a mixture of nitrogen and oxygen, with just a trace of carbon dioxide and other gases.

With this atmosphere, the first animal life began. From it, over a very long time, higher forms of life developed. The earth became the small but remarkable planet that we know, the only one in our solar system that supports a wide variety of life.

The earth today is basically nothing more than a ball of rock covered mostly by water and surrounded by an envelope of air. Yet there are many things about our planet that make it just right for supporting life.

The earth circles a star that is a steady producer of the light and heat needed by life. Unlike many other stars, ours does not flare up or dim. It shines

Earth's atmosphere, seen from Gemini 7, *appears as a rim on the horizon. The sun has set, but its image can still be seen because its rays are bent as they pass through the air.*

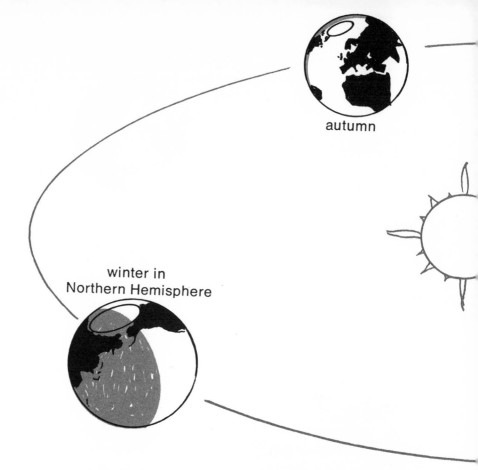

autumn

winter in
Northern Hemisphere

steadily, and its gravitational field is also steady. The sun's pull on the earth hardly varies at all, and so the earth travels the same orbit year after year.

The orbit is a good distance from the sun. The earth is close enough to the sun to be warmed by it, but not so close that it bakes in the sun's rays. Then, too, the earth's movements in orbit regularly warm and cool the surface of our planet.

The earth spins on its axis, an imaginary line running through its center. (The North and South Poles are the places where the axis emerges from the earth.) Because of the spin, the earth has day and night. The sun appears to rise, travel across the sky,

14

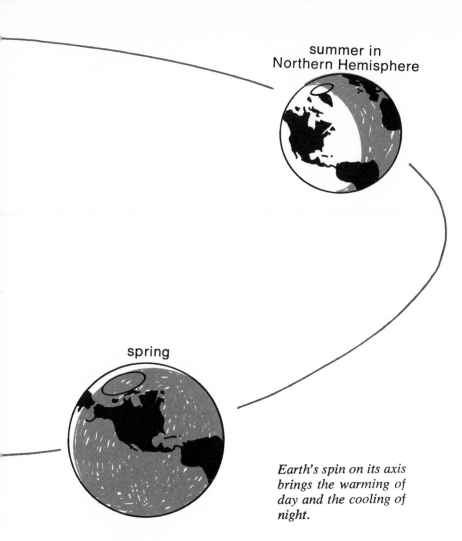

summer in
Northern Hemisphere

spring

Earth's spin on its axis brings the warming of day and the cooling of night.

and set. Different parts of the earth are warmed by day and cooled by night. As it spins, the earth is also revolving around the sun. Because its axis is tilted, the earth has seasons. As the earth journeys around its orbit, each pole is tipped toward the sun for part of the year. The Northern Hemisphere has summer when the North Pole is tipped toward the sun. It has winter when the North Pole is tipped away. The changing seasons give different parts of the earth a

15

chance to warm up or cool off, and most of the earth is kept at relatively even temperatures. Only the polar regions are very cold, and only the regions at the equator are very hot.

The earth's magnetic field is extremely important to life. Something inside the earth makes our planet act like a giant bar magnet, with invisible magnetic lines of force arching from one magnetic pole to the other. These lines of force form the earth's magnetic field, and the space around the earth is filled with them. They act as a trap for electrically charged particles from the sun and other sources in space.

Earth's magnetic field

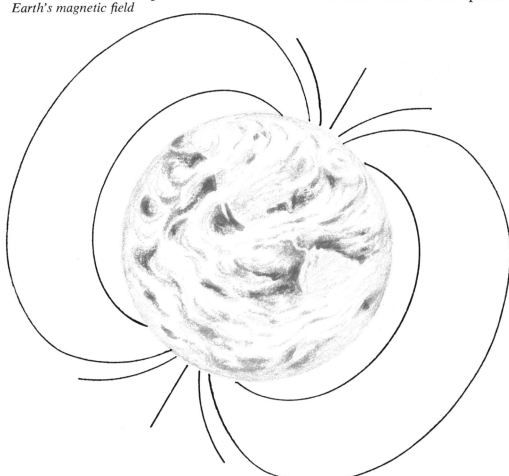

Without the magnetic field, these high-energy particles would bombard the earth, probably making most kinds of life impossible.

The atmosphere is still another thing that makes the earth a planet of life. We could not live without the atmosphere. It is the air we breathe: the source of oxygen for animal life and of carbon dioxide for plant life. It is the source of rain. It is the blanket that traps part of the day's heat from the sun and keeps it from escaping at night. It is the shield that protects us from the sun's ultraviolet radiation and other dangerous rays.

The atmosphere is held captive by the earth's gravity, and the earth's gravity is something else that is just right. The strength of gravity is determined by a body's mass, by the amount of matter in it. The earth's gravity is strong enough to hold an atmosphere, but not so strong that it holds a dense atmosphere. The earth's atmosphere is thin enough for light to pass through.

For all these, and other, reasons, the earth is a planet of life. Moreover, it is a planet of very varied forms of life, life of the land and sea and air. It supports this wide variety for still another reason: the earth itself is in a sense alive.

The earth is a restless, changing planet where new land forms and mountains are thrust up. If this were not so, the earth would not be inhabited by man and other creatures of the land. Its continents and islands would long ago have worn away, leaving only an ocean to cover the surface of the earth.

Land is constantly being eroded, or worn away,

17

Erosion in the Goreme Valley, Turkey, left small rocks balanced on the tops of rock pedestals.

by some of the very things that make the earth a planet of life. The winds of the atmosphere, the rain and snow, the running streams, the frost and ice of winter—all erode the land. Slowly and steadily land is worn away and washed into the sea. Just as steadily, the oceans wear down the coasts.

Yet the sea does not conquer the land. It does not spread over the face of the whole earth. Continents and islands change, but they continue to rise above the water. The reason is that the earth is stirring inside, and so the crust keeps changing. As it is ever being worn down, so is it ever being rebuilt.

The energy that stirs the earth is heat. This has always been so. Heat within the young earth shaped our planet by causing eruptions, which added rock to the surface, gases to the atmosphere, and water to the oceans. If the earth had had only the heat of its

18

early years, it would by now be cold and dead inside, for all its heat would have vanished into space. But the earth still stirs because there is another source of heat. This source is radioactivity.

Several of the earth's chemical elements—such as thorium, uranium, and potassium—are radioactive. That is, their atoms give off parts of themselves in the form of atomic particles. The particles carry energy, which takes the form of heat. The amount of heat produced by radioactivity is small. But it is produced steadily and its escape through the earth's crust is slow, because rock is a poor conductor of heat. So the heat accumulates, or builds up, within the earth. Over hundreds of millions of years, the heat becomes very great.

This heat is the energy that keeps our planet alive and changing. Earth scientists do not yet know exactly how the changes occur. They are not sure how the continents formed or how mountains are built. They see volcanoes pouring forth new rock, but they do not know precisely why volcanoes erupt. In the same way, they know that the earth's stirring causes earthquakes, but they cannot wholly explain the quakes.

Earthquakes, like volcanic eruptions, can bring disaster to large numbers of people. But they are a price to be paid for a planet that is alive inside, for a planet where land life can exist. And so these signs of our planet's inner activity are of great interest to earth scientists.

Facts about the Earth

Size and shape: Since very early time people have wondered about the shape of the earth. At first they thought the earth was flat. Some 2,500 years ago, scientists of ancient Greece took a large step forward. They concluded that the earth was a sphere, that it was round. About 300 years ago Isaac Newton suggested that the earth could not be perfectly round. He thought the earth's spinning must cause it to bulge at the equator and be flattened at the poles. Gravity measurements later proved him right. Gravity is stronger at the poles than at the equator, because the poles are closer to the center of the earth. The earth's diameter measured at the poles is about 27 miles smaller than at the equator. The average diameter at the poles is 7,899.83 miles, while at the equator it is 7,926.42 miles. Modern studies with man-made satellites show that the earth bulges in some places and has depressions, or dips, in others. No one yet understands why that is so, but scientists now describe the earth as "an imperfect sphere."

Area: The earth has a surface area of nearly 197 million square miles. More than 70 percent of this area is covered by oceans. For unknown reasons there is more land in the Northern Hemisphere than in the Southern Hemisphere. North of the equator oceans and seas cover 60 percent of the surface; south of the equator they cover 80 percent.

Age: The earth is thought to have condensed from a cloud of gas and dust 4.5 billion years ago.

3   When the Earth Shakes

This section of 4th Avenue in Anchorage dropped 20 feet during the 1964 Alaskan earthquake. The opposite side of the street was unaffected.

Shortly after 5:30 in the afternoon of March 27, 1964, Alaska was hit by a major earthquake. In Anchorage, people first felt a slight tremor that flicked through the city. Buildings creaked. Small objects danced on the shelves in stores. Instants later the everyday life of the city took on the unreality of a nightmare.

Automobiles began to whip back and forth across the streets. They bounced up and down on their tires like so many rubber balls.

In a big modern department store the floors heaved like the decks of a ship caught in a storm. Great chunks of the outer walls crashed to the street.

On 4th Avenue a movie theater dropped 30 feet

21

A residential section of Anchorage after the quake

straight down into a hole that opened beneath it. A florist's shop snapped in two. The street shifted and buckled. Sections of it dropped 20 to 30 feet, carrying along cars, shops, and telephone poles.

At Turnagain, a residential area overlooking Cook Inlet, people rushed from their shaking houses. Beneath their feet the earth shook and jolted. It churned and crumbled and sank away. It cracked into blocks separated by deep crevices. Trees fell. Whole houses were ripped apart. The front of the

22

bluff collapsed, taking with it houses, garages, cars, trees, and pieces of road.

Seen from the air, Alaska's largest city looked as if a careless giant had strode through it. Buildings on one side of a street might be crushed, tumbled, or upended, while those on the other side were whole and in place. An otherwise level road would suddenly drop off into a jumble of sunken pavement. The airport control tower was a heap of broken glass and twisted steel girders, but the terminal building still stood.

Anchorage was only one victim of the earthquake's shock waves. Along a span of 500 miles the earth shook and heaved. Mountains shuddered, loosing avalanches of snow and rock. Railroad tracks were bent and twisted like strips of tinfoil. Highways billowed and crumbled. Houses were shaken to pieces.

The worst blows of all came from the sea. Mountainous masses of water, set in motion by the earthquake, rushed into bays and inlets along Alaska's jagged coast. There they piled up into towering walls of water that broke upon the land. Boats were snatched up and hurled inland, buildings smashed, and piers carried away.

Then suddenly it was all over. Except for the twitches of aftershocks, the land lay still.

Although they have learned a great deal about earthquakes, earth scientists still have many questions about what causes them. They know that the basic cause is the earth's internal heat, the energy that powers all the activity within the earth. It somehow creates the forces that result in earthquakes. Exactly what those forces are or how they are created no one knows. But earth scientists do know what the forces do and how they cause earthquakes.

The unknown forces place severe stress on rock of the earth's crust or of its upper mantle, the layer that lies beneath the crust. For a time, the rock may flow or bend under this pressure, for it is slightly plastic. But if the pressure builds to a certain point or if it suddenly increases, the rock snaps and then springs back into place. Sometimes the rock snaps near the earth's surface, leaving a telltale crack, which is called a fault. Sometimes the rock snaps far below the surface, leaving no fault that we can see. Either way, when the rock snaps, an earthquake occurs. The snapping releases the pent-up energy of the rock. The energy is instantly changed to shock waves that make the earth quake, or tremble.

The shock waves travel out in all directions from the focus, which is the part of the fault where the quake starts. Some waves travel deep into the earth. Others are waves that travel over the surface. It is the surface waves that do the damage, and the amount of it depends on several things.

One is the depth at which the earthquake occurred. Most quakes take place within the upper 15 miles of the earth's crust. But earthquakes can and do take place in the upper mantle. A few occur as much as 460 miles deep in the earth. The deeper earthquakes tend to do less damage, because their shock waves lose energy while traveling toward the surface.

24

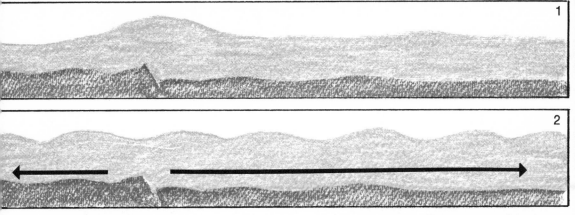

A second is the violence with which the rock snaps. Sometimes rock snaps readily. Then little energy is released. At other times rock has been under great pressure before it faults and a huge amount of pent-up energy is released.

A third is the area most affected by the quake. Heavily populated areas are likely to suffer more damage than those with few people and buildings. Then, too, much depends on the buildings and their foundations. If the buildings are solidly constructed on solid ground, they may withstand a severe earthquake with little damage. Otherwise, they may collapse like houses of cards.

When a fault snaps on land, damage stems only from the shock waves sent out. But sometimes a fault snaps along the ocean floor. It may set up what many people call "tidal waves." This is not, however, a very good name, since the waves have nothing to do with tides. Scientists prefer to call these waves *tsunami,* a Japanese word meaning "harbor waves."

This is how the waves take shape. If an undersea fault snaps up and down, a huge, low mound of water suddenly forms at the ocean surface. The mound is leveled by gravity into a series of broad waves that travel at speeds of up to 500 miles an

How a tsunami forms: 1. a mound of water forms when a fault snaps; 2. waves travel out from the mound; 3. (page 26) when the low waves reach the shallower waters near shore, they pile up into a massive wall of water.

25

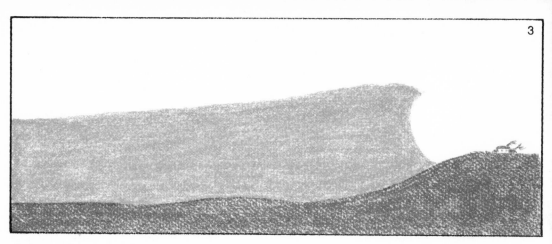

A tsunami can reach a height of 60 feet. Here it dwarfs the houses on shore.

hour. Ships at sea are not affected by these waves. The waves are at most two or three feet high, and each is separated from the next by a hundred or so miles. Nevertheless, each broad low wave holds a vast amount of water. When a wave reaches the shallower water near shore, the front part of the wave is slowed. The back of the wave piles up on the front, and the long low wave changes to a massive wall of water. Rolling through a harbor or inlet, a tsunami may be anywhere from six to 60 feet high. This wall of water breaks on shore, crashes over the land, and then draws back, sucking buildings and boats with it. The first tsunami may be followed by a second and a third.

In Alaska's 1964 earthquake, the fault ran both through the land and through the ocean floor. First the earth shook with terrible violence. Then tsunami formed.

At Valdez, a small port that lies at the head of a narrow inlet, stevedores were unloading a ship when the earthquake struck. The earth's shaking was followed by a wall of water that rushed up the inlet, broke over the land, and swept out again. The pier, the stevedores, and the onlookers vanished with the wave.

26

At the port of Kodiak the water first rose smooth and fast in a silent flood that reached far over the land and then withdrew. The flooding served as an urgent warning, and Kodiak's people headed for the hills behind the town. In the harbor, crab and salmon boats bucked at their moorings as the water rose and were grounded when it withdrew. Then the sea came back. It came back as a 30-foot-high wall of water that thundered into the harbor, picked up 100-ton fishing boats, and flung them into the town. Retreating, the water carried off crab and salmon canneries, boats, shops, and houses.

Seward was even harder hit. A small port and railroad terminus, Seward had a tank farm, for the storage of oil. When the quake hit, the storage tanks exploded. Fire roared along the waterfront. Then a 50-foot-high tsunami rushed up the bay, broke over the waterfront, and picked up the burning oil. A fiery flood of water surged inland at 100 miles an hour. It snatched up locomotives, freight cars, oil drums, boats, buildings, and the pier. It hurled them into the town, crushing buildings, flattening automobiles, and crumbling telephone poles. When the

A boat carried inland and left behind by the tsunami at Kodiak

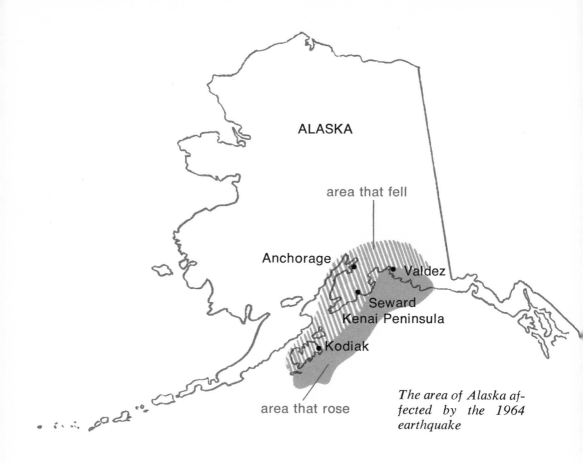

ALASKA

area that fell

Anchorage

Valdez

Seward
Kenai Peninsula

Kodiak

area that rose

The area of Alaska affected by the 1964 earthquake

water withdrew, it carried along so much burning material that the bay was lighted up for miles that night.

The 1964 earthquake was so powerful that several years later scientists were still measuring its effects with astonishing results. They found that in two to four minutes it had drastically changed the face of Alaska. A region the size of Maine was lifted three to eight feet by the earthquake, while another region of the same size sank. An island was lifted 33 feet. On Kenai Peninsula whole mountains shifted side-

28

ways by five feet and sank seven feet.

The same earthquake made itself felt all over the world. Its shock waves stirred the water at Key West, Florida, nearly 4,000 miles away. Surges of water were felt along the coast of the Gulf of Mexico between 30 and 40 minutes after the quake. As water surged in and out, three ships at Houston, Texas, snapped their moorings. At New Orleans a sudden rise of one and a half feet in the Mississippi River caused other ships to break their moorings.

The movement of the earth created waves in the atmosphere that were felt in many distant regions. In Georgia, for example, water levels in wells were pumped up and down by 10 to 20 feet because of these atmospheric waves.

Shock waves in the earth itself caused Houston to bob up and down by five inches and slopped water from swimming pools. In faraway Iran, the land moved up and down a third of an inch as waves from the Alaskan earthquake passed.

The waves from a major earthquake have tremendous energy. Those that pass through the earth travel at speeds of several miles a second. They may surface thousands of miles away from the earthquake center. They may make the whole earth vibrate like a giant bell.

Because of their travels deep within the earth, such waves have become the most valuable tool that scientists have for studying the earth's interior. In fact, most of what is known about the inside of the earth has come from the study of earthquake waves.

An X-Ray Picture
4 of the Earth

The deep interior of the earth lies far beyond man's reach, and no light waves penetrate it to show us what lies within. But earthquake waves do penetrate the inside of the earth, and so for earth scientists they have become messengers of a sort. When the waves reach the surface, their arrival is recorded by delicate instruments at seismic observatories. ("Seismic" comes from the Greek word *seismos,* meaning "earthquake.") These records, when coupled with information about the waves themselves, yield clues to the regions through which the waves have passed.

Every seismic wave is a kind of giant push. It is a push that is passed from one rock particle to the next, much as a push can be passed through a line of

30

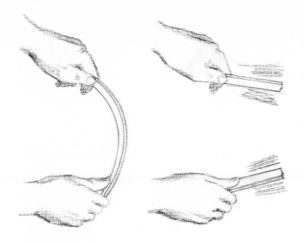

You can get some idea of what happens when rock snaps under pressure by slowly bending a thin ruler between your hands. As you keep applying pressure, the ruler keeps bending. Finally the strain becomes too great and the ruler snaps. When the pent-up energy of the ruler is released, the ends fly straight and vibrate. Waves are set in motion in the air. Particles of air push other particles and so the waves, or pushes, pass through the air.

people. The rock snaps and releases energy, which is immediately changed to waves, or pushes. Rock particles push the rock particles ahead of them, and those particles push still other particles. In this way, the waves pass through the earth, although the rock itself stays in place.

When an earthquake occurs, two kinds of wave are set in motion.

One is a compression wave, which can be described as a push-pull wave, because it moves the rock particles forward and backward, pushing and pulling them. Compression waves travel at speeds of four to eight miles a second.

The other is sometimes called a torsion (twist) wave, or shear wave. If you put a pencil between your palms and move one palm forward, the pencil will rotate, or twist. In much the same way, rock particles between the two surfaces of a fault are twisted between the slipping surfaces. These particles send a torsion wave through the earth. A torsion wave travels at about half the speed of a compression wave—at speeds of 2.5 to 4.2 miles a second.

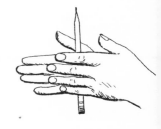

31

Minutes after an earthquake has occurred, waves start arriving at seismic observatories. Because they travel faster, the compression waves arrive first. That is why they were named primary waves, or P waves, some years ago. The slower torsion waves arrive second, and so they were named secondary waves, or S waves.

As each wave reaches an observatory, instruments register its arrival and record the exact time of arrival. Later these records are sent to one of the world's several centers for earthquake information, where reports from different observatories are compared and studied.

By studying the records of many, many earthquakes, earth scientists have learned much about how seismic waves travel through the earth: about the speeds at which they travel and the paths they follow.

For example, the speed of a wave changes with the density of the rock through which it is passing. The speed increases as the rock grows denser; that is, it increases in rock where the particles are packed more closely together. The speed decreases in rock that is less dense. The speed of a seismic wave is also affected by the elasticity of the rock through which it is passing.

Like light rays, seismic waves may be refracted (bent) or reflected. They are refracted when they pass through materials of changing density and elasticity, as light rays are on entering water. They are

32

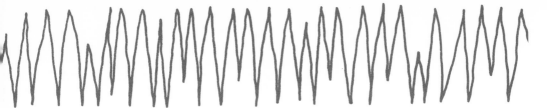
S waves

reflected from a surface, as light is from a mirror. When waves travel from one kind of material into another, some are reflected back toward the earth's surface. The rest travel on into the new material.

Then, too, there are important differences in the travels of P waves and those of S waves. As well as differing in traveling time, they also differ in the materials that they can pass through. A P wave can travel through solids, liquids, or gases. An S wave can travel only through solids.

Armed with such information about seismic waves, earth scientists have been able to "explore" the interior of the earth. The waves have given them a sort of x-ray picture of the earth we never see.

This picture shows that the earth has three main regions: the core, the mantle, and the crust. The core is at the center of the earth. The mantle surrounds the core. And the crust, the outermost region, surrounds the mantle.

We live on the crust, but we see very little of it. In the long, long life of the earth, great layers of sediment have been laid down on top of the crust, as wind, rain, frost, and chemical erosion pried loose tiny fragments of rock. The crust, however, is the only region of the earth that scientists can readily reach. They have learned that it is made mainly of two general types of rock: one has the properties of granite, the other of basalt.

The upper part of the continents is made of relatively light rock. Its most familiar form is granite

33

and so the name "granite" is often used to describe the upper part of the continents. Continental crust is usually 22 to 37 miles thick. The crust beneath the oceans is thinner, being three to three and a half miles thick. It is made of much denser rock, often called basalt, the name of its most familiar form. Seismic waves travel through basalt at higher speeds than they do through granite. So do the waves from man-made explosions, which scientists also use for exploring the crust.

The boundary where the crust ends and the mantle begins was discovered in 1909 by a Yugoslav seismologist. In his studies of seismic waves he found that at depths of about 20 to 40 miles their speed

Cross section of the earth

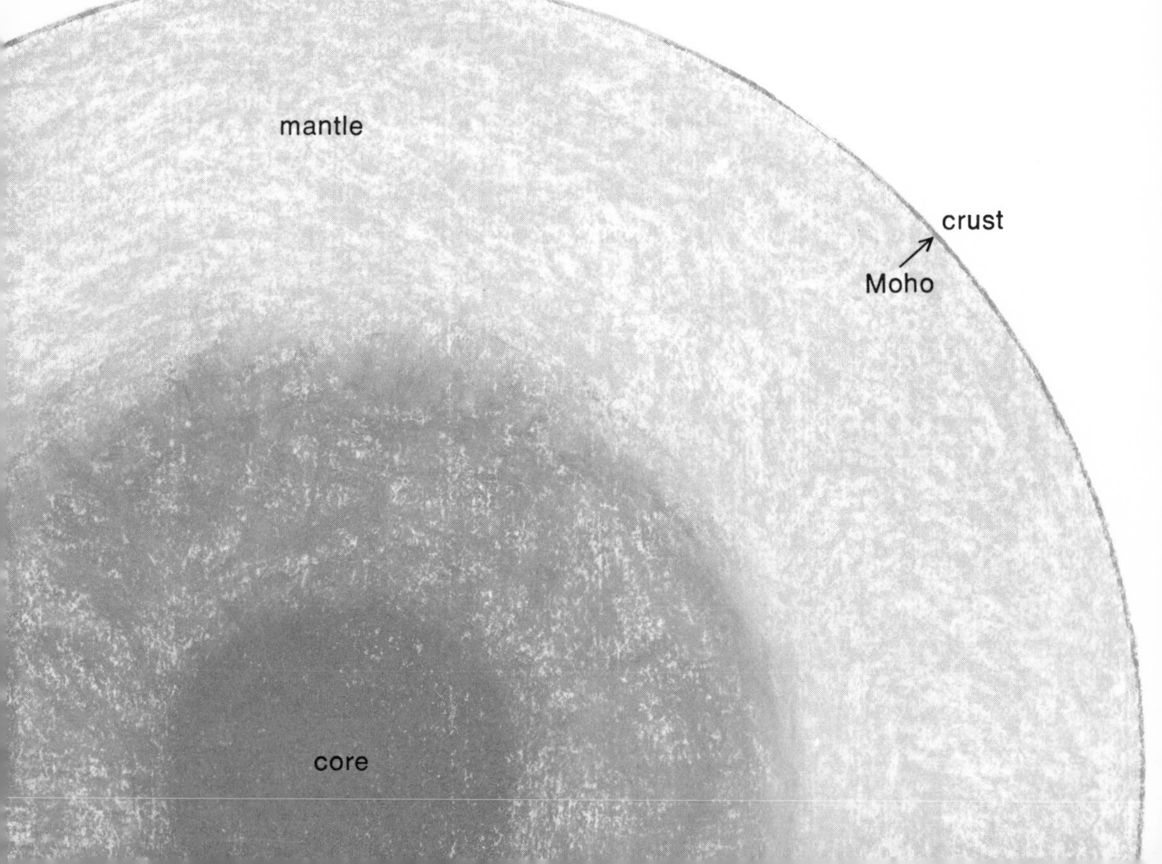

mantle

crust

Moho

core

increased sharply. The waves seemed to be entering a zone of much denser rock. In other words, he found that the earth's crust is a thin layer that ends abruptly a few miles down. The place where it ends, the base of the crust, was named for its discoverer. Its full name is the Mohorovičić discontinuity, but it is usually called the Moho. Above the Moho is the crust. Below it is the mantle. At the Moho the speed of seismic waves suddenly increases as they enter the denser mantle.

The mantle seems to be layered, for at different depths some waves are reflected back to the surface. The material of the mantle is rock that is probably rich in iron and magnesium. But it is not rock as we know it. Scientists think that at least some of the rock is under such great pressure that it bends and flows like thick tar. They consider the mantle a solid, however, because both P and S waves travel freely through it.

The waves travel freely through the mantle to a depth of about 1,800 miles. There a change of material occurs, and waves are reflected to the surface. At that depth the core begins.

Some years ago seismologists made a very interesting discovery about the core. It happened this way.

They had drawn up timetables for the travel times of P waves and S waves. The table showed, for example, that P waves travel a distance of 1,000 miles in 3 minutes 22 seconds. S waves travel the same distance in 6 minutes 03 seconds. The difference in their travel time is 2 minutes 41 seconds.

Sample from a Timetable for P and S Waves

| Travel Time | | | | Difference in | | Distance from Source |
For P Waves		For S Waves		Arrival Times		(miles)
3 min. 22 sec.		6 min. 03 sec.		2 min. 41 sec.		1,000
5	56	10	48	4	52	2,000
8	01	14	28	6	27	3,000
9	50	17	50	8	00	4,000
11	26	20	51	9	25	5,000
12	43	23	27	10	44	6,000
13	50	25	39	11	49	7,000

From thousands of measurements, seismologists have learned that P and S waves follow regular travel schedules for distances up to 7,000 miles. They have therefore worked out timetables for these waves. The difference in arrival times can be translated into the distance between the seismic observatory and the source of the earthquake.

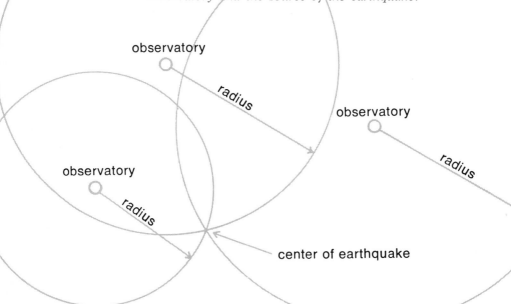

Suppose three observatories translate their arrival-time differences into distances, and each uses its distance as the radius of a circle. The place where the three circles cross is the center of an earthquake.

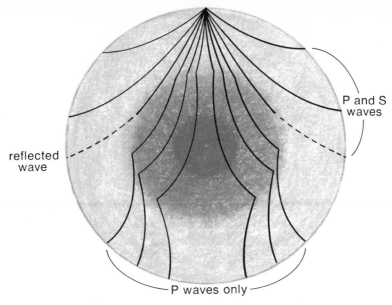

reflected
wave

P and S
waves

P waves only

Therefore if S waves arrive at an observatory 2 minutes 41 seconds after the P waves, seismologists know that an earthquake has occurred 1,000 miles away. These tables worked very well for locating earthquakes, except at observatories that were more than 7,000 surface miles from the site of the earthquake. At these observatories the P waves were late in arriving and the S waves never arrived at all.

Seismologists realized that the strange case of the late P waves and the missing S waves was a clue to the interior of the earth. They reasoned that to reach these distant observatories waves had to pass through the core of the earth. The core, or at least the outer part of it, was clearly made of material that S waves could not pass through. This meant that it could not be a solid. It was unlikely to be gas, since gas probably could not support the pressures existing at that depth. Therefore, the region was most likely molten, or liquid. The behavior of P waves also fitted into this picture. They were traveling at slower speeds, as they would if they had passed from a solid into a liquid, and were sharply bent.

37

When P waves have traveled about 1,350 miles into the core, another change takes place. Again some waves are reflected. Others speed up and are sharply bent. Scientists think this means that the earth's core has two regions, an inner core and an outer core. The outer core is a molten layer about 1,350 miles thick. The inner core has a radius of 790 miles. It seems to be solid and made of dense metal. Scientists estimate that it is probably 90 percent iron and 10 percent nickel.

They also think that the core must be under enormous pressure and extremely hot. The outside of the inner core is probably under 45 million pounds of pressure per square inch. Its temperature is probably well over 5,000 degrees Fahrenheit.

There is, of course, no way to sample the materials of the core. There is no way to measure the pressure or temperature. But laboratory experiments yield clues to conditions in the core.

For example, scientists have long known that the temperature required to melt something increases with the pressure on that material. This was dramatically demonstrated a number of years ago in a "hot ice" experiment at Harvard University. Ice was placed under 600,000 pounds of pressure per square inch and heated to above the boiling point of water. Yet the ice did not melt.

No laboratory can create the great heat and pressure that exist within the earth. But scientists can create increasing amounts of pressure and measure the melting points of iron or other material as the pressure increases. When their findings are plotted

38

on a graph, the points form a curve. By extending the curve, scientists can estimate what conditions are 3,000 miles within the earth. That is how they have arrived at their figures for heat and pressure at the inner core.

The mantle and the lower crust are also hot. But here there is more direct proof.

The deeper men dig into the crust the higher the temperature rises. Some of South Africa's deep gold mines have had to be air-conditioned to make it possible for men to work them. Deep oil wells reach rock that is hotter than 212 degrees Fahrenheit, the boiling point of water at sea level. When volcanoes erupt, their lava—the molten rock that comes from within the earth—may have a temperature of up to 2,000 degrees.

Heat in the mantle is apparently hot enough to melt any kind of rock we know, but the rock is also under very great pressure. As a result, it acts like a solid. S waves can pass through it—to depths of about 460 miles—and the rock can snap and cause earthquakes. At the same time, there are ways in which the mantle behaves like a very gummy liquid. For example, the earth's crust floats on the mantle and can move up and down in it. Hawaii moves up and down about four inches when the moon, passing overhead, exerts its greatest gravitational pull. During an ice age, land areas that lie under a great burden of ice are pressed down into the mantle. As the ice later melts, they slowly rise.

The mantle therefore seems to be a solid that sometimes acts like a liquid. Earth scientists think that large regions of the mantle, although solid, may be very close to their melting point and therefore capable of plastic flow. In fact, recent studies of seismic waves indicate that the uppermost layer of the mantle is much more plastic than scientists had earlier realized.

To many earth scientists it seems likely that movement in the mantle accounts for the stresses and strains that result in earthquakes. They further think that the same movement accounts for volcanoes. They think so because most of the world's earthquakes occur in the same regions as most of the world's active volcanoes.

Each year the earth is shaken by at least ten major earthquakes and millions of small ones. Of the small ones about 150,000 are strong enough to be felt by anyone standing near the earthquake center. By mapping earthquake centers for many years, seismologists discovered that most quakes occur in certain belts, or areas, of the world. In other parts of the world earthquakes are almost unknown, but along these belts the earth stirs and shakes. And along the same belts volcanoes erupt, often with tremendous violence.

Earthquake Prediction

There is no way to prevent an earthquake from happening. When strain builds up within the earth, it must be released. Earth scientists think, however, that it should be possible to predict earthquakes and issue warnings, much as weather scientists now issue hurricane and tornado warnings. They are therefore studying earthquake-prone regions in an effort to learn whether there are measurable changes that can be used to predict major quakes.

In such studies earth scientists use many kinds of delicate instruments. Some, for example, record changes in the earth's magnetism. If the changes are worldwide, they tell nothing about earthquakes. But if there are brief changes in the magnetism of a small area, this seems to indicate movement in the earth. Other instruments record the tilt of the land. In many earthquake regions land tends to tilt slowly, rising in one area and sinking in another. Soviet and Japanese scientists have noted abrupt changes in the tilt rate shortly before severe earthquakes occurred. Still other instruments measure strain and slippage along an existing fault.

In the United States most of these studies have been made in California, along the San Andreas fault, which cuts across the coast north of San Francisco and runs southward for 600 miles. It passes

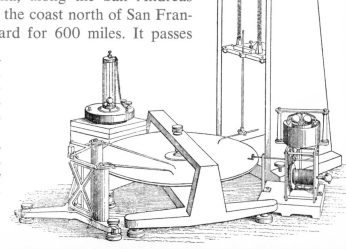

A seismometer—an instrument for recording movements of the earth. The three pens hold steady above a coated glass plate that moves with the earth. When the earth and plate move, the pens trace the up-down, east-west, and north-south motions in the coating.

The San Andreas fault near San Francisco

fault

through San Francisco and to the east of Los Angeles.

For thousands, perhaps millions, of years this part of the earth's crust has been split to a depth of about 30 miles. From time to time slippage occurs along the fault, with the western side sliding northward. Two or three times a year the western side creeps northward a fraction of an inch, and the earth trembles a little. But there are times when the western side jumps northward by as much as 30 feet, causing a major earthquake. One of these really big jumps took place in 1857. A somewhat smaller jump in 1906 brought San Francisco down in ruins.

Since 1857 the section of the fault near Los Angeles has been "locked" in place, and since 1906 the same thing has been true of the section near San Francisco. Between these two sections is a third where constant small slippages take place, showing that the fault is still active.

In the middle 1960s seismologists began installing sensitive instruments along a 200-mile section of the fault. Readings from the instruments were transmitted directly to the National Center for Earthquake Research at Menlo Park, California. By 1968 earth scientists at the center were studying the readings with deep concern, for these indicated that the land near San Francisco was under considerable strain. They hoped that the strain would be released in a series of small quakes but feared its sudden release in a major quake. But there was nothing they could do except to wait and see if they had read the signs correctly.

42

The course of this stream in Southern California has been displaced 450 feet to the right where it crosses the San Andreas fault.

Two 60-year-old fences, parallel and about 20 feet apart, have each moved 31 inches to the right where they cross the San Andreas fault.

5   When Volcanoes Erupt

February 20, 1943, began like any other day for a Mexican farmer named Dionisio Polido. He rose before dawn, ate breakfast, and set out for the corn-field he was planning to work. Almost immediately he discovered that this day was strangely different.

The ground felt hot beneath his bare feet, though the sun had not yet had time to warm it.

Several times he thought he heard thunder, but the sky was clear with not a cloud in sight.

By October 1944 Paricutín had almost finished growing, but ash and lava were still flowing at the base of the cone.

Stranger yet, a column of smoke was rising from the far end of his cornfield. Wondering what could have caught fire, Polido hurried over to beat out the flames. But the smoke was not coming from a fire. Instead, Polido saw that the very ground had cracked open and a smoking, gray-white material was bubbling out of the crack.

Polido fled, sure that the world was coming to an end. But, as he later learned, what he had seen was the birth of a volcano. Its name is Paricutín.

In the days following its birth, Paricutín erupted with enormous violence. The opening in the cornfield grew into a long crack with a pear-shaped hole at one end. Smoke, sparks, and ashlike material bil-

46

Fields and farm buildings buried in ash from Paricutín

lowed out of the crack. Glowing rocks the size of automobiles were hurled from the hole. Paricutín poured forth so much material that in only five days' time it built a 300-foot-high cone. Within a week, lava oozing from the great crack in the ground had advanced over a mile of land. It swallowed two villages, burying them so deep that only the church steeples remained in sight. All the people who had farmed and lived in the area were moved away.

By the time Paricutín was a year old, it stood 1,410 feet high. Then its growth began to slow. When the eruptions stopped on February 25, 1952, the volcano was some 1,500 feet tall.

Paricutín lies in one of the highly volcanic areas

47

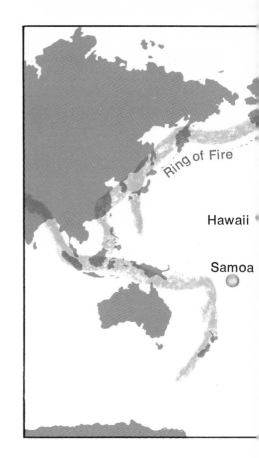

Earthquake belts

of modern times. Most of today's active volcanoes are found in two great belts. One belt circles the Pacific Ocean and is sometimes called the "ring of fire." The other belt runs more or less east-west from Indonesia to the Mediterranean Sea. In these same belts most of the world's earthquakes take place.

The Pacific belt takes in volcanoes of the Andes Mountains in South America and of Central America and Mexico, with a branch into the Caribbean. The belt runs north through the Cascade Range of northern California, Oregon, and Washington. It continues in Alaska, the Aleutian Islands, Kam-

48

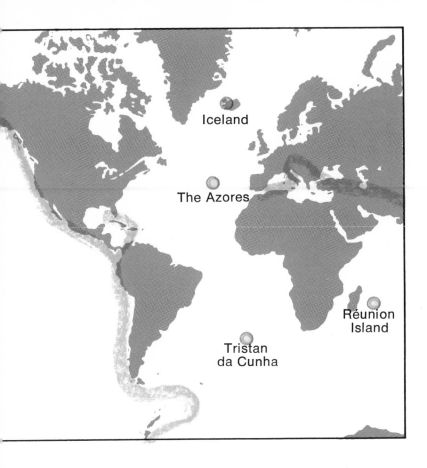

Iceland

The Azores

Réunion Island

Tristan da Cunha

chatka, Japan, the Philippines, New Guinea, and New Zealand. In the east-west belt there are volcanoes in Indonesia, Armenia, Turkey, southern Greece, and Italy.

Outside of the two belts, a few other places also have volcanoes. In the Pacific there are mid-ocean volcanoes in Samoa and Hawaii; Réunion Island in the Indian Ocean is volcanic; so are Iceland, the Azores, and Tristan da Cunha in the Atlantic. Eastern Africa has active volcanoes, which lie along the chain of lakes near the great Rift Valley. Antarctica's Mount Erebus is also an active volcano.

Most of these volcanoes are mountains that took shape long ago. Some are very active, while others have been quiet for so long that no one is sure whether they are extinct (dead) or simply dormant (sleeping). But every now and then a new volcano comes into being as Paricutín, and later Surtsey, did. These new volcanoes are of great interest to volcanologists, earth scientists who specialize in volcanoes.

Volcanologists would like to know more about the basic causes of volcanic eruptions. They wonder why volcanoes are found in some places and not in others. They wonder why a place such as Britain, which was the scene of huge eruptions 70 million years ago, has no live volcanoes today. They would like to know why some volcanoes seem to erupt without warning, while others give such clear signals that their eruptions can be predicted with great accuracy. They would like to know whether volcanoes such as those in the Cascades are extinct or dormant.

Volcanologists are also interested in the materials that come out of volcanoes, for these have traveled to the surface from a part of the earth that we cannot see. They have formed from molten rock called magma.

No one knows just how, why, or where magma forms inside the earth. Earth scientists think that masses of magma exist about 40 miles below the earth's surface, but they cannot be sure. The magma may—or may not—be part of the mantle. Why it should be molten is another puzzle. Perhaps it is rock that is superheated, that for some reason is hotter than the surrounding rock. Or perhaps it is not hotter but is under less pressure.

However it forms, magma is molten rock that contains gases and the crystals of minerals that are forming in it. The chief gas is steam, but magma also has carbon dioxide and other gases. Usually the crystals are dissolved in the magma, which tends to be very hot, much as crystals of salt or sugar are dissolved in boiling water. The gases may also be dissolved, or they may occur as bubbles. In these ways, odd as it may seem, magma is something like soda pop.

Soda pop contains sugar. You can taste the sugar, but you cannot see it, because the crystals are dissolved in the liquid.

Soda pop also contains a gas, carbon dioxide, which makes the bubbles in it. If you hold an unopened bottle of soda up to the light, you will not see any bubbles. The carbon dioxide is dissolved in the liquid. If you open the bottle gently, you will see some bubbles. The gas is slowly separating out of the liquid as bubbles. If, however, you shake the bottle before opening it, the gas will rush out, carrying along a spray of liquid. The harder you shake the bottle, the more violent the explosion will be. As long as the cap is on the bottle, the pressure of the gas is contained. When you remove the cap, the pressure is released and the carbon dioxide suddenly expands, causing a small explosion. The soda pop erupts out of the bottle.

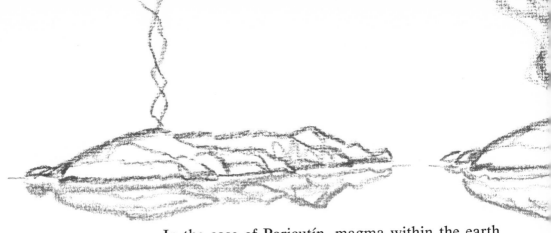

In the case of Paricutín, magma within the earth was pressing against the rock of the crust. It forced its way into a crack that happened to lead to Dionisio Polido's cornfield. As magma entered the crack, its gases expanded, widening the crack. Then, with the way out charted, a white-hot column of magma blasted its way to the surface.

As magma reaches the surface, it changes. The gases separate out of it, and mineral crystals usually form. And so its name changes, too. The molten material at the surface is called lava, as is the rock that forms when liquid lava freezes, or hardens.

Paricutín's eruption was violently explosive. Magma shot to the surface. It tore loose rocks from the crust and hurled them into the air. Liquid lava was torn apart by expanding gases. It hardened in the air and fell to earth as volcanic ash and bubbly chunks called cinder. A hill of cinder and ash rapidly built up around the vent, or opening, in the ground. Meanwhile, lava flowing from a nearby crack in the ground buried the Polido farm and advanced toward the neighboring villages.

Paricutín is an example of one kind of violent eruption. But there are several other kinds.

Some violent eruptions are caused by steam. Water, heated by magma, changes to steam and

52

therefore expands both suddenly and greatly. The result is an explosion. That was what happened to the Japanese volcano Bandai-san in 1888, when steam blew out a whole side of the mountain.

Magma, however, was responsible for one of the greatest explosive eruptions in history. It took place at Krakatoa, a volcanic island that is now part of Indonesia.

In late May of 1883 explosions began in one of Krakatoa's three cones. They did not seem violent or dangerous, and so no one was alarmed. People from a neighboring island even hired a steamer and made a sightseeing trip to the cone. For the next three months rumblings and explosions were heard, but nothing happened.

Early in the afternoon of August 26, a big explosion took place. It was followed by others. A black cloud formed above the island and stretched miles into the sky. The next morning at 10:20 a gigantic explosion blew two of the cones to bits with a roar that was heard 3,000 miles away. Columns of ash and pumice soared into the air, plunging the region into darkness. The sea was choked with rafts of pumice. Dust was blown into the atmosphere in such quantities that it cut off heat from the sun and caused a two-year drop in world temperatures. The

53

Tuff

Cinder

Pumice

Products of Volcanoes

As magma reaches the surface, it changes to **lava.** That is the name used both for molten material on the surface and for the rock that forms when that material freezes, or hardens.

Gases separate out of the magma. They are also a product of volcanoes.

As the molten rock cools, **crystals** may form. If the rock cools slowly, the crystals may be as big as an inch across. If it cools quickly, the crystals will be small. If it cools very quickly, crystals may not form at all. Instead the molten material freezes into **glass.** A common form of this natural glass is **obsidian.** Lava is usually made of crystals or glass or both.

Sometimes lava flows quietly out of an erupting volcano. It forms streams of molten rock, which are called **lava flows.**

Sometimes eruptions are violent, as expanding gases cause explosions. Gases rushing out of the vent carry along pieces of rock. Some are solid and others are liquid. The fragments fall to earth, forming **pyro-**

dust drifted slowly three times around the world, showing its presence in brilliant red sunsets.

The eruptions destroyed most of the island. They also destroyed parts of nearby islands. But the islands were not blown into the sky. Instead, they collapsed into the sea. Such a huge quantity of material had blasted out of the earth that the islands were undermined and sank.

A very different kind of eruption took place in 1902 on the French island of Martinique, in the

54

clastic (fire-broken) **rock,** or **tephra.** Some pyroclastic rock is old rock torn from the earth's crust or from the vent of the volcano. Some is liquid lava, torn apart by the expanding gas. It may still be liquid when it falls to earth. More often it freezes in the air. This lava may take several forms.

One form is made up of tiny particles called **volcanic dust.** Some volcanic dust is so fine and light that when it is blasted high into the air, it stays there for years and may float all the way around the earth.

Fragments the size of sand are called **ash.** They are often cemented by water into a hard rock called **tuff.**

Sometimes liquid lava is puffed up into a froth by the expanding gases within it. This bubbly rock is called **cinder.** If it is even more bubbly and puffed up, it is called **pumice.** Pumice is so bubbly that it floats in water.

Some pieces of lava take on a rounded shape while flying through the air. A rounded piece of newly hardened lava is called a **bomb.** A piece with sharp corners is called a **block.**

Bomb

Block

West Indies. In early spring Mount Pelée had started to stir. Smoke and steam drifted out of its vents. Deep-throated rumblings were heard. By April gray, powdery ash was falling like light snow on the city of St. Pierre at the foot of the mountain. It crunched under carriage wheels in the streets, coated the furniture in houses, and found its way into kitchen cupboards. From time to time small earthquakes shook the city. In the first week of May explosions were heard.

55

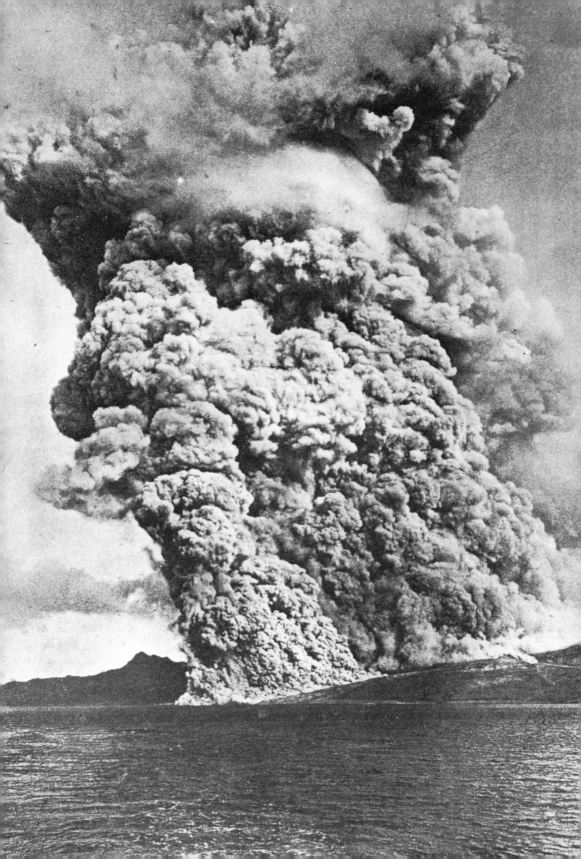

In December 1902 Mount Pelée erupted again and the cloud of ash reached a height of 13,000 feet. The city of St. Pierre was completely destroyed in the May 8 eruption.

The morning of May 8 dawned, bright and clear. At 7:52 a.m. Mount Pelée erupted. An explosion tore out one side of the volcano. Officers on a ship in the harbor saw a great black jet shoot out of the mountain and grow into a boiling, black cloud. In less than a minute the cloud had swept over the city and harbor, swallowing everyone and everything in its path. In another minute or so, the cloud had passed. St. Pierre was a flaming ruin. The harbor was filled with ships that were overturned and sinking. And some 30,000 persons were dead. They had been killed by the heat and gases of the cloud.

This kind of eruption is called a glowing avalanche. It is called an avalanche because of the great mass of red-hot rock fragments that rush along beneath the cloud. Each fragment is giving off gas, and the gas forms a kind of shell around the fragment. It holds each fragment away from the others. It holds the bottom fragments off the ground, and so there is almost no friction to slow the fragments. That is why a glowing avalanche moves at speeds of a hundred miles an hour. The glowing rock fragments set fire to whatever the cloud passes over. In 1915 a glowing avalanche rushed down Mount Lassen in California, setting fire to and destroying an entire forest.

The glowing avalanche left St. Pierre in ruins.

The house near the bridge was built on top of the mudflow that buried Herculaneum. The ruins beneath it were discovered in the early 1700s and the cementlike mud was removed.

An ash flow is a somewhat similar kind of eruption. In it volcanic ash forms and each piece is surrounded by a shell of expanding gas. The whole mass of ash flows very freely.

Glowing avalanches and ash flows can cause mudflows, if the materials in them are mixed with water from, for example, a heavy rain. The mixture be-

Ruins of a bakery in Herculaneum

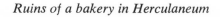

comes a giant flow of mud. Most mudflows, however, form when heavy rains fall on loose cinder and ash. It was a mudflow of that kind that buried the Roman town of Herculaneum in the year 79.

That August Mount Vesuvius erupted with enormous violence. A hail of tiny bits of pumice buried the town of Pompeii. A layer of ash fell on top of the pumice, and then water from a heavy rain cemented the ash into tuff. The same rain fell on the ash, pumice, cinder, and bits of lava that covered the upper slopes of Vesuvius. The mixture turned to mud that swept down the mountain. Herculaneum, which had escaped the hail of pumice but lay in the path of the mudflow, was completely buried.

Street of shops in Pompeii, with Mount Vesuvius in the background

Although many of the world's volcanoes erupt violently, there are others that erupt quietly. Two of these are Mauna Loa and Kilauea on the island of Hawaii. Mauna Loa, which reaches up some 30,000 feet from the floor of the Pacific, is the tallest mountain in the world and still growing. Every few years an eruption adds more lava to it. When these volcanoes erupt, there is no explosion. Instead, long fissures, or cracks, open up. Fountains of liquid lava spurt into the air, and lava flows fairly slowly from the fissures.

Because they erupt both gently and fairly often, these two volcanoes have been studied closely and steadily by scientists from the Hawaiian Volcano Observatory. The observatory is built on the rim of Kilauea Crater. It is one of a number of volcano observatories in various parts of the world.

Volcanologists go about their work in many ways. They study quiet volcanoes and visit volcanoes that are erupting. They collect gases and minerals from erupting volcanoes. They measure the strength of the gravitational and magnetic fields. Their aim is to understand volcanoes. They want to know how volcanoes work, what they are like inside, and whether it is possible to control mudflows, lava flows, and volcanic gases. Most of all, they want to be able to predict eruptions. They want to be able to say when and where an eruption will take place and what kind of eruption it will be. Only in this way can the people who live near volcanoes be protected. And people will always live near volcanoes, for volcanoes have given the earth some of its most fertile soil.

Scientists at the observatories keep a constant watch on their volcanoes. One of the instruments they use is the seismograph, which records the light earthquakes that occur when magma moves beneath a volcano. Another instrument is the tiltmeter, which indicates the tilting of land as magma wells up below. A magnetometer records changes in magnetism. This is another clue to what is happening, since most of the earth's solid rocks are lightly magnetized but molten rock has no magnetism.

Through such studies, volcanologists in Hawaii have sometimes been able to track the build-up of an eruption, as they did at Kilauea Iki, a crater on Kilauea.

Kilauea had been quiet for several years. Then in October 1958, a series of light earthquakes began and went on for several months. They were a sign that magma was moving inside the mountain. By spring of 1959 the mountain was beginning to bulge near the crater. By summer the swelling was down, but in August a swarm of small earthquakes took place. Their starting point showed that magma was traveling channels that led to the mountain. The

61

Fountains of lava reached heights of more than 1,500 feet at Kilauea Iki in November 1959.

mountain began to swell again. By November it was swelling fast and the earthquakes were stronger than ever. Magma was tearing rock apart within the mountain.

A half-mile-long fissure opened on the side of Kilauea Iki. Lava poured out of it and into the crater. It soon formed a lava lake 335 feet deep. The eruption stopped, started again, and stopped. The lava drained down its vent like water draining out of a bathtub.

Fountains erupted from the crater, squirting glowing lava hundreds of feet into the air. After each eruption the lava drained back down its vent. Over a period of five weeks some 133 million cubic yards of lava erupted in fountains, and some 85 million cubic yards of it drained back into the mountain. The rest formed a lava lake in the crater. Tiltmeters showed a tremendous swelling of the mountain. Clearly, something was going to give way.

Another swarm of earthquakes told what was giving way. The source of the earthquakes was moving steadily eastward. This meant that magma was splitting rock within the earth and forcing its way east. Volcanologists tracked the earthquakes to the village of Kapoho and warned the people to leave. The warning came just in time. That very evening the land sank several feet and began to rock back and forth. As darkness fell, a three-quarter-mile-long fissure opened up beside the town. Lava spurted from it in glowing fountains. Before the eruptions ended 36 days later, lava flows had covered the village and 2,500 acres of farmland.

In other parts of the world volcanologists have also had great successes in predicting eruptions and moving people away in time. Yet there have also been many failures. In September 1965, for example, Taal volcano in the Philippines blew up, killing 190 persons. But the monitoring station beside the volcano had registered no signs of what was about to happen, even though it was equipped with instruments to record earthquakes, changes in the tilt of the ground, and changes in magnetism. Only one clue had been noted: a rise in the temperature of the lake within Taal Crater. For some years the temperature of the water had been a steady 91 degrees Fahrenheit. In late July it rose to 113 degrees, but it dropped slightly a few days before the eruption. Even the place where the mountain burst open did not become hot beforehand. The place was a rice field, and its healthy, green crop had showed no sign of withering, as it would if the ground had become hot. Yet this was where the volcano blew up with an explosion that left a mile-long crater and buried the monitoring station in ten feet of ash.

Even in Hawaii volcanologists are sometimes taken by surprise. For example, an eruption at Makaopuhi Crater in December 1965 was almost completely unexpected. It took place at a time when the volcano was only slightly swollen, and a warning swarm of earthquakes occurred only one hour before the eruption.

In spite of their successful predictions, volcanologists know that they have much to learn about eruptions, and they may never fully understand volcanoes until they understand the forces that make the earth alive. Then they may also understand how and why patterns of volcanic activity have changed.

Ancient lava flows show, for example, that at one time or another there have been volcanoes in almost every part of the world. There are traces of volcanoes in New England, New York, New Jersey, and Michigan. There are signs of volcanic eruptions in Great Britain, Sweden, and Australia, as well as many other places where there are no volcanoes today. So one of the puzzles of the past is why the regions of volcanic activity have changed.

Then, too, in the past the earth had many flood eruptions. These are the greatest eruptions known, and they build not mountains but broad plains and plateaus. In these eruptions huge floods of very liquid lava pour out of fissures in the earth's crust. Single flows may spread over hundreds or thousands

64

of square miles. The Columbia Plateau of Oregon, Washington, and Idaho was built by flood eruptions, and it covers some 100,000 square miles. In places the lava rock is 5,000 feet thick. Iceland was built by flood eruptions. There lava covers more than 200,000 square miles and is 9,000 feet thick. Although these eruptions were apparently common in the past, they are almost unknown today. The only one we have a record of is a 1783 flood eruption in Iceland.

In the past, volcanic eruptions were among the great builders of the earth's surface. They built plains and plateaus as well as mountains. Today eruptions build only mountains.

These volcanic mountains are found in the most active parts of the earth. In the same regions most of the world's earthquakes take place. And here, too, rocks of the earth's crust have most recently been crushed together and lifted up into mountains. That is, volcanoes are found in the same regions as the earth's young folded mountains. The same thing seems to have been true in the past. There is evidence that in ancient times most volcanoes were in areas where folded mountains were being built or had recently been built.

Many earth scientists think that these three activities—eruptions, earthquakes, and mountain-building—are related to a fourth: the building and renewing of continents. There is evidence that mountain-building plays a large part in adding to the continents, those great blocks of rock that rise above the oceans.

Mauna Kea in Hawaii is a shield volcano. The summit of this gently sloping volcano reaches 14,000 feet.

Types of Volcanic Mountains

Volcanic mountains have three main shapes. The shape of the mountain is determined by the shape of the vent and the kind of material that pours out of it.

Some mountains are built chiefly by liquid lava that pours out of long fissures in the sides of the volcano. The lava flows pile up, forming a broad, gently sloping mountain. Such a mountain is called a **shield volcano,** because it is shaped like a shield laid flat on the ground. The Hawaiian volcanoes, which are the largest on earth, are shield volcanoes. There are shield volcanoes in northeastern California and in parts of Oregon. There are many small shield volcanoes in Iceland.

Cinder cones reach heights of 500 to 1,000 feet. Barcena, on San Benedicto Island off the western coast of Mexico, is one of the tallest.

An explosive eruption may pile up a big hill of cinder and ash around the vent. The hill is shaped like a cone with the point cut off and so is called a **cinder cone.** The top of the cone forms a bowl-shaped dent called a crater. The crater takes shape

because the explosions tend to blow away material from the vent. While the cone itself is being built of cinder and ash, lava may flow out at its base. Some cinder cones occur alone. Others are found on the sides of bigger volcanoes. Particutín is one of hundreds of cinder cones in the state of Michoacán, Mexico. The western United States has many cinder cones, among them Sunset Crater in Arizona and Mount Pisgah in southern California.

The third type of volcano is built both of lava flows and of cinder and ash. It is called a **composite volcano.** (The name means that it is made of various materials.) A composite volcano develops because more than one kind of eruption occurs. For example, a volcano may start by erupting like a shield volcano, with flows of liquid lava. The next time it erupts, it may erupt like a cinder cone, laying down layers of cinder and ash. Its third eruption may consist of lava flows. Most of the world's famous and beautiful volcanoes are composite volcanoes. Among them are mounts Hood, Rainier, and Shasta in the United States and Mount Fuji in Japan.

Popocatepetl, a composite volcano, looms more than 17,000 feet over the Mexican landscape.

6   Continents and
       Folded Mountains

"Why does the earth have land?" sounds like the kind of question a small child might ask. It is also the kind of question earth scientists ask. They wonder why light rock should be bunched together on some parts of the earth and not on others. In fact, they wonder why land masses exist at all, for continents are the exception, not the rule, on our planet.

68

Nearly three quarters of the earth is covered with oceans, under which lies a crust of basalt.

In a few places, though, huge chunks of granite rise above the oceans, forming continents. The continents are something like icebergs, with only their tops showing. Most of an iceberg's bulk is hidden beneath the water. Most of a continent's bulk reaches down into the mantle. Earth scientists consider that the continents float in the mantle, much as icebergs float in the sea.

Scientists think the continents float in the mantle as icebergs float in the sea, with great granitic roots going down into the mantle.

It is also true, of course, that all of the crust floats in the mantle. And this fact offers a kind of answer to the question of why the earth has continents. The granite, being lighter rock, floats higher than the basalt.

But that is only a partial answer. It does not explain where the granite came from, how it reached the earth's surface, or why the continents happen to be where they are.

Earth scientists think that the granite started to form when the earth was very young and still so hot that no hard crust had developed on its surface. Heat and pressure caused many chemical changes to take place inside the earth. Chemical compounds were built up and broken down and built up again. Inside the earth, granitic materials began to form. There are several theories about what happened next.

One theory says that when the earth began to cool near the surface, the basaltic material became solid first. This dense material then sank toward the bottom of the cooling mass, while lighter material rose. The lighter material hardened into granite, forming the continents.

70

A second theory says that the earth's earliest crust was all basalt. In time, stresses and strains within the earth caused the basalt to fracture, or crack, in some places. Hot materials from inside the earth flowed out through the fractures, and these materials became the continents.

A third theory is based on the idea that currents of heated material are rising in the mantle, cooling, and sinking, much as water turns over when it is heated in a pan. Water at the bottom of the pan heats first. The heated parts expand, become lighter, and rise. As the heated parts reach the surface, they move around in swirls, giving up some heat to the cold water at the surface. Then they are pushed aside by warmer water rising from the bottom. Now cooler and denser, the first parts sink.

These movements set up what is called a convection current. In a convection current, warmer material from the bottom keeps rising, while cooler material from the top keeps sinking. Convection currents usually occur in pairs. They rise together, flow away from each other, and then sink.

The third theory about the continents assumes that temperature differences within the earth set convection currents in motion. Perhaps a current starts where the hotter core meets the cooler mantle, or perhaps it starts in some other way. In any case, greater

Convection currents in heated water

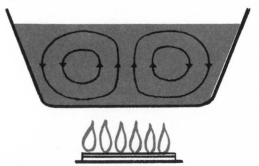

heat in one part of the mantle could cause an upward flow of hot rock. It could cause giant convection currents, measuring thousands of miles in diameter and flowing at a rate of perhaps an inch or two a year.

According to this theory, convection currents within the young and molten earth carried both granitic and basaltic material to the surface. The currents spread out, cooled, and sank. However, the light granitic material was not carried down in the sinking currents. It was left behind on the surface, like a kind of scum. As the currents continued to rise, they carried up more and more granitic material and swirled it around at the surface. In time, this material hardened into great blocks of granite. Since the granite was lighter than the other rock around it, it floated higher in the mantle.

Some scientists think that huge swirls of granite

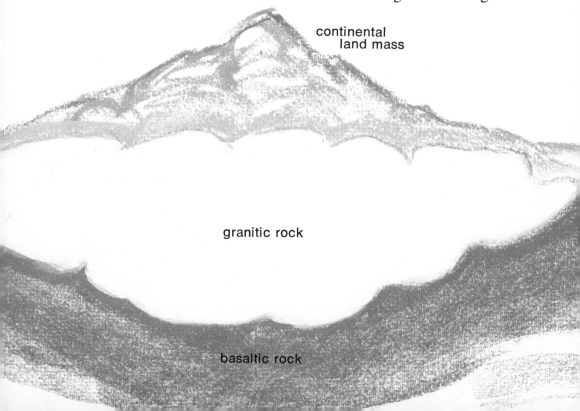

continental
land mass

granitic rock

basaltic rock

accumulated in several places and became the earliest continents. Other scientists think that all the granite accumulated in one place, forming a huge supercontinent that later broke up. These scientists suppose that in its early stages the earth had only one gigantic pair of convection currents in the mantle. Later these two large currents broke up. Other, smaller currents formed and tore apart the supercontinent.

By whatever means, the continents did form. Today they are land masses of relatively light granitic rock, probably with a base of basalt. They rise well out of the seas, but they do not end where the seas wash their shores. Shelves of continental rock reach out into the water, sloping gently down. When the continental shelves are about 600 feet below the surface of the sea, they end abruptly. A continental slope plunges sharply down to the ocean floor. These slopes are the true boundary between the continents and the oceans.

Studying ancient rocks, earth scientists have concluded that the first great blocks of granite must have formed between 3 and 3.5 billion years ago. The most ancient rocks they have found have an age of about 3 billion years.

continental shelf

ocean

sediment

slope

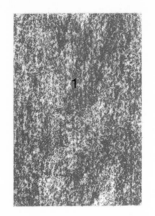

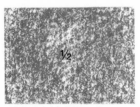

after 14 billion years

after 28 billion years

Scientists arrive at such figures by a method called radioactive dating. It enables them to measure the time that has passed since minerals in the rocks crystallized. The method involves a complex analysis of radioactive elements trapped in the crystals as they formed.

All elements are made up of atoms, the basic building blocks of matter. But in radioactive elements, atoms break down and radiate, or give off, tiny particles. Because they are giving off particles, the atoms themselves are changed. They become atoms of another element. For example, atoms of a variety of uranium called uranium-238 break down eventually forming atoms of a variety of lead called lead-206. Atoms of uranium-235 break down to form atoms of lead-207. Thorium-232 forms lead-208. Rubidium-87 forms strontium-87, and potassium-40 forms argon-40.

The rate at which a radioactive element decays, or breaks down, is called its half-life. An element's half-life is the time required for half its atoms to decay. Thorium-232, for example, has a half-life of 14 billion years. That is, it would take 14 billion years for half the atoms in a given amount of thorium to

74

decay into atoms of lead-208. It would take another 14 billion years for half of the remaining atoms to decay into lead, and so on. Each of the radioactive elements has its own half-life.

The atoms of radioactive elements move about freely in molten rock. When the rock cools to a certain temperature, crystals form. The crystals may be crystals of granite, but trapped in them are atoms of other elements. The atoms of radioactive elements begin to decay immediately that the crystals form.

Therefore these atoms serve as a built-in clock. By analyzing rock and measuring the amounts of, for instance, thorium-232 and lead-208, scientists can calculate how long the process of decay has been going on. And so they can tell the age of the rock.

In studying and dating the rocks of the continents, earth scientists discovered an interesting pattern. In Africa they found several areas with very ancient rock. Each area was surrounded by belts of younger rock. The ages of the very ancient rocks ranged from 2 to 3 billion years. The rocks in the younger belts had an age of 600 million years or less.

At least, much of the rock in the belts was fairly young. A closer look showed that the rock in the belts was of mixed ages. Along with the young rock, the belts contained large blocks of rock that was the same age as the very ancient rock. Apparently, sections of the crust were bent, folded, and warped some 600 million years ago. As this was happening, molten material from beneath forced its way into the folds and hardened into new rock.

The pattern suggests that the continents are regularly renewed. They are worn down by wind, water, ice, and chemical erosion, and so they become lighter and float higher in the mantle. But before they are completely eroded, new material is added to them along their edges. There is evidence that the new material takes—and has always taken—the shape of belts of mountains. And this idea fits well with what is known about mountain-building.

To our eyes the world's mightiest mountains seem unchanging and unchanged, for a man's lifetime is not even a second in the life of these mountains. Yet they are forever changing. They are thrust out of the crust in upheavals that twist, bend, fold, and upend layers of rock. Fragment by fragment, grain by grain, they are sculptured and worn down. Over hundreds of millions of years towering, jagged peaks are worn into low, rounded mountains, which in time are worn down to their very roots. Although we do not see the building-up or the wearing-down of great mountains, we can see the difference between young mountains and old. In North America the soaring, craggy peaks of the Rockies are the mark of young mountains. The rounded, gentle slopes of the Appalachians are the mark of older mountains.

Earth scientists think that mountains have been thrust up and worn down ever since a solid crust formed on the earth. In fact, the oldest rocks known seem to be the roots of ancient mountains. They also think that the earth goes through periods of mountain-building. These periods are called revolutions, and in the earth's history there have been at least ten of them. One was the Appalachian Revolution,

The Alps in Switzerland

The Appalachians in New York State

Folded rock in the Chugach Mountains, Alaska

Fish fossil found on Mount Lebanon, Syria

which began between 200 and 300 million years ago. The most recent is the Cascadian Revolution, which began about 60 million years ago and produced the Rockies, the Andes, the Alps, and the Himalayas. These are all folded mountains that have buckled out of the crust. They are the world's mightiest chains of mountains. And they are the mountains scientists least understand.

Earth scientists have seen volcanic mountains grow. They have seen erosion etching high plateaus into mountains. They can see where the earth has faulted and where blocks of mountains have been uplifted, forming ranges of fault-block mountains, such as the Wasatch Range in Utah and the Sierra Nevadas. But the folded mountains—these are the giants that the human eye cannot catch in action. These are the mountains whose secrets men have sought for years.

About 200 years ago scientists first probed the world's big mountains to find out what they were made of. The answer was a surprising one. Rocks had formed from sediment that had been washed from the land into shallow seas, packed together, stirred and changed under tremendous heat and pressure, and then somehow thrust skyward. The

78

proof was twofold. First, there was the nature of the sedimentary rocks. Nearly all were the kinds that form in shallow seas—sandstone, shale, limestone. Second, the rocks contained fossils of sea life, traces of creatures and plants that live only in shallow seas. Since some of the fossils were found several miles up the mountains, it was clear that the rocks—and the mountains themselves—must have risen from the seas. They must have risen from shallow inland seas or from shallow ocean basins bordering the continents. Further studies showed that the same thing was true of all the world's great chains of mountains.

Every great mountain range has beds of sedimentary rock that formed in shallow seas. The rock is folded, faulted, and tilted. It appears to have formed from deposits of sediment that were at least 30,000 feet thick.

In addition to sedimentary rock, every huge mountain range seems to have a massive core of granite or other rock that formed from molten rock.

It is also true that many of the great mountain ranges border on or parallel the coasts of continents.

Considering these and other facts, many earth scientists have tried to work out theories to account for the earth's folded mountains. An early theory suggested that beneath its solid crust, the earth was cooling and shrinking. A shrinking mantle would cause the crust to wrinkle, fold, and buckle, just as the skin of a withering apple is forced into ridges and folds as the pulp inside shrinks. This theory accounts for the forces that could tilt and fold beds of rock and thrust them up into mountains. But even so, most earth scientists today feel that the theory cannot be true. They doubt that the earth is cooling and shrinking. And they do not see how the theory can account for the way mountains are distributed on the earth's surface.

A number of theories have been based on the idea that the folded mountains must have grown from ocean basins filled with sediment. It is supposed that sediment from the land washed into shallow ocean basins bordering the continents or into inland seas. Here the earth's crust was slowly being warped downward. As the weight of sediment grew greater and greater and the down-warping continued, the floor of each basin sank. Thus the water in a basin was never more than 1,000 feet deep, as indicated by the fossils found in the sedimentary rock. But sediment was able to accumulate in the basin to a depth of 30,000 to 50,000 feet. The name for such a sediment-filled basin is geosyncline. Earth scientists have supposed that a geosyncline might be more than a thousand miles long and hundreds of miles wide. They have also thought that whole series of geosynclines must have paralleled the coasts of continents.

Over millions of years, they said, sediment from the land was washed into geosynclines, and the geosynclines went on sinking. But when the geosynclines were several miles deep, the sinking stopped. The sediment was then somehow crumpled, folded, squeezed, and pushed up into mountains. As the mountain-building was taking place, magma entered the lower parts of the geosyncline and formed the granite cores of the mountains. Sometimes lava flows added to the mountains.

Although no one had ever seen a geosyncline, earth scientists agreed that they were possible and that they would account for the materials of folded mountains. The difficulty lay in accounting for the forces within the earth that could squeeze the geosynclines, tilting and folding rock, and that could thrust up mountains. There are many theories about these forces, but no one is generally accepted.

Recently a number of earth scientists have turned to a very different idea. They think that the chains of folded mountains are caused by the crumpling of continental borders. They are convinced that both the continents and the ocean floors are moving and that the movements cause continental edges, continental shelves, and ocean sediment to be crumpled into chains of mountains. Their thinking is based on discoveries made during recent explorations of the ocean floors.

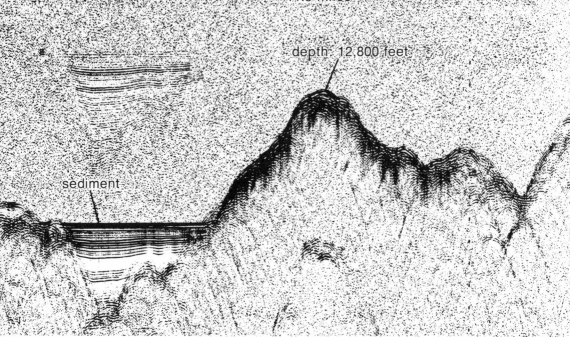

11.5 miles

depth 12,800 feet

sediment

Profile of part of the Mid-Atlantic Ridge. The sediment in the depression at left is 2,500 feet thick.

7   Ridges and Rifts

Oceans cover 71 percent of the earth. Yet until a few years ago, scientists knew more about the face of the moon than they did about the ocean floors. The reason was that they could see the moon. Only in recent years have they been able to probe the ocean depths with echo sounders, deep-sea cameras, and other modern instruments.

This exploration of our planet's unknown face showed that the earth's most rugged features lie beneath the oceans. Here are the tallest peaks and the deepest depths. Here, too, is a gigantic mountain range that circles the earth.

Oceanographers, scientists who study the oceans,

82

had known for some time that there were ridges rising from the ocean floors. What they had not realized was that these ridges are linked into one huge underwater ridge, or mountain chain, that runs along the bottom of every ocean in the world. The ridge runs south from the Arctic through the middle of the Atlantic Ocean. Near Antarctica, the ridge swings eastward around South Africa, branches into the Indian Ocean, and loops around Australia. It continues across the Pacific and reaches up the west coast of the Americas.

Overall, the mid-ocean ridge is 40,000 miles long and hundreds of miles wide. Its rise from the ocean floor varies between 1,000 and 10,000 feet, but it has peaks that are 20,000 feet high. The tallest peaks break through the ocean surface and form islands.

The ridge is the greatest mountain range on earth, but it is unlike the giant ranges found on the continents. It is made of masses of volcanic lava and not of folded sedimentary rock, as the great continental mountain ranges are. In addition, in many areas the ridge has a rift in its middle; the rift is a cracklike valley that runs along the crest of the ridge for most of its length. Although the ridge forms one huge mountain chain, it is not continuous. Rather, it is cut into sections a few hundred miles long by fracture zones, which shift the sections out of line with one another. The ridge is a mid-ocean center of earthquakes and of volcanic activity.

At the base of the Mid-Atlantic Ridge there are low, lumpy hills that level off into flat plains. The

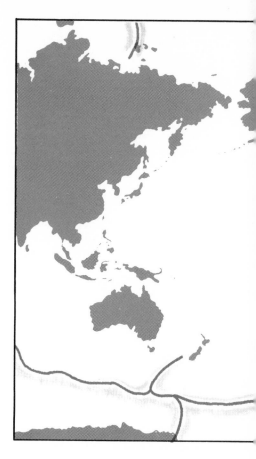

plains are the continents' dumping ground. Here currents drop huge amounts of sediment washed from the land. The sediment spreads out on the plains, which reach for miles on end across the Atlantic floor. Together with the remains of small sea creatures, the sediment has settled to the bottom, hiding the rugged layer of rock below. At the edge of the plains the continental slopes rise sharply.

The bowl-shaped Pacific is much more rugged than the Atlantic. It has almost no plains. Instead, the floor is rough with hundreds of seamounts, or guyots, which are drowned island volcanoes, scores of mountain ranges and island chains, and a number

84

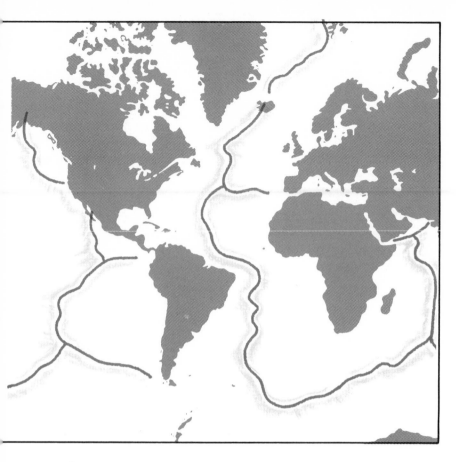

of deep trenches. The trenches, which are rare in other oceans, are all very much alike. They are long and narrow and extremely deep. The Tonga-Kermadec Trench is long enough to stretch from Kansas City to New York City; it is seven times deeper than the Grand Canyon. Among the other great trenches of the Pacific are the Aleutian, Kurile, Japan, Mariana, Philippines, and Java trenches, which rim the northern and western sides of the ocean. Two great trenches of the eastern side are the Acapulco and the Peru-Chile. The trenches are never found alone. They are always alongside land or next to an island arc, which is a curved string of islands.

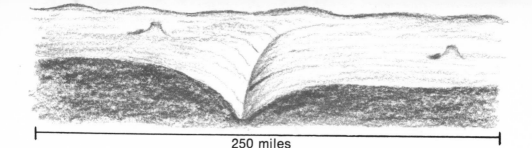

250 miles

A trench in the Pacific Ocean floor

Oceanographers had explored the ocean floor to answer a question: what is it like? But, as is often true in science, the answer to one question immediately raises new questions and brings to light new problems. Exploration of the earth's unseen face confronted oceanographers with a number of very large puzzles.

They wondered what the trenches were, how they had formed, and why the deeper ones all reached a common depth of about 35,000 feet. The distribution of the trenches was also extremely interesting. Nearly all of them lay around the rim of the Pacific, paralleling the ring of volcanoes and the high, young mountains. They lay in the areas where the strongest earthquakes take place. And the deepest and steepest trenches were in places where earthquakes occur at great depths in the earth.

Another major puzzle had to do with the apparent youth of the ocean floor. When they dated samples drilled from the ocean floor, oceanographers found only relatively young rock. The floor of the ocean seemed to be far younger than the continents and than the very waters of the oceans themselves. The same thing was true of the seamounts. Because there is little, if any, undersea erosion, mountains on the ocean floor should last forever. Yet oceanographers could find no ancient seamounts. Like the ocean floor, the seamounts were made of young rock.

Then there was the question of the missing sediment. For as long as land and sea have existed, sedi-

86

|⊢───⊣|
500 miles

ment from the land has been washed into the sea. *Part of the Mid-*
And so oceanographers had expected to find a layer *Atlantic Ridge*
of sediment several miles thick. The layer found was
only about one-tenth that thick. The fossils in the
sediment sampled were all surprisingly recent. They
show that the oceans contain no sediment that is
more than 150 million years old and very little that
is more than 80 million years old.

Although oceanographers had not made enough
studies to be sure, they began to think that something unexpected was happening on the floors of the
oceans. It seemed as if the ocean floors were in some
way being renewed.

The ridge-and-rift system was no less puzzling.
Oceanographers were faced with finding an explanation of this earth-circling submarine mountain range
and its rifts. The rift in the Mid-Atlantic Ridge
averaged 6,000 feet deep and was eight to 30 miles
wide. This rift, like the others, appeared to be a
place where the earth had cracked open or been torn
apart. The earthquakes and the volcanic activity
showed that the ridge and rifts were a sign of great
forces still at work within the earth. What could the
forces be?

To a number of earth scientists the ridge-and-rift
system suggested convection currents. Here, they

87

thought, currents might be rising in the hot rock of the mantle, spreading outward from the ridge under the crust, and tearing apart the ocean floor into great rifts. Heat-flow measurements supported the idea. They showed that the flow of heat along the ridge was much greater than the flow observed on the continents and elsewhere on the ocean floors. Along the Mid-Atlantic Ridge the flow was two to eight times greater. At the Easter Island Rise, which is part of the mid-ocean ridge in the Pacific, the heat flow was five times greater.

Similar measurements were made of heat flow in the trenches. It was much smaller than average, about one tenth of the flow on the ocean floor. At the bottom of a trench that parallels the Pacific coast of South America, the heat flow was one thirtieth of what it had been at the Easter Island Rise. The trenches seemed to be places where cooler, denser material was sinking and pulling down the ocean floor.

As various scientists considered the evidence in favor of convection currents, they began to develop a new theory, which fitted the facts and explained many of the puzzles that had turned up on the ocean floors. This is the theory of ocean-floor spreading.

According to this theory, paired convection currents of hot material slowly rise in the mantle. Near the top they turn and flow away from each other under the crust. Where the rising currents separate, they break the rock of the crust and pull it apart into great rifts. Molten material from the mantle flows as lava through these rifts and builds a ridge.

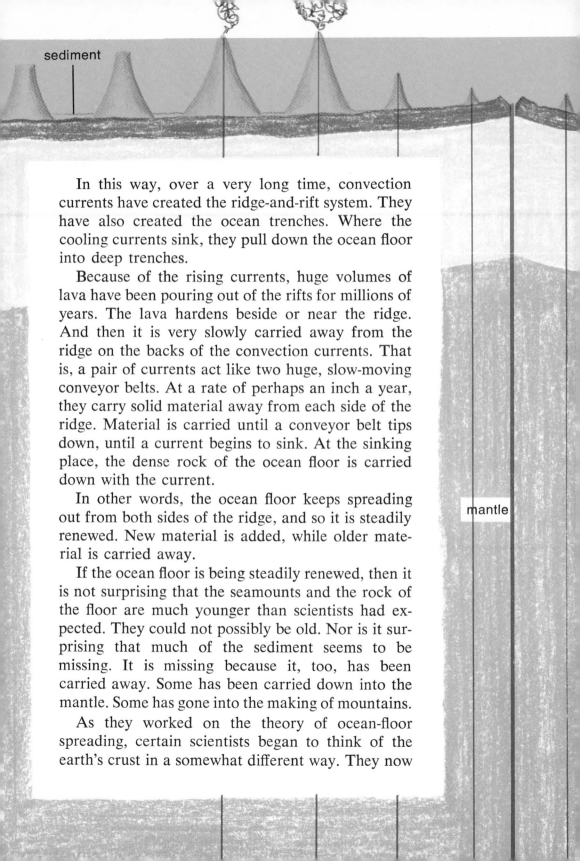

sediment

mantle

In this way, over a very long time, convection currents have created the ridge-and-rift system. They have also created the ocean trenches. Where the cooling currents sink, they pull down the ocean floor into deep trenches.

Because of the rising currents, huge volumes of lava have been pouring out of the rifts for millions of years. The lava hardens beside or near the ridge. And then it is very slowly carried away from the ridge on the backs of the convection currents. That is, a pair of currents act like two huge, slow-moving conveyor belts. At a rate of perhaps an inch a year, they carry solid material away from each side of the ridge. Material is carried until a conveyor belt tips down, until a current begins to sink. At the sinking place, the dense rock of the ocean floor is carried down with the current.

In other words, the ocean floor keeps spreading out from both sides of the ridge, and so it is steadily renewed. New material is added, while older material is carried away.

If the ocean floor is being steadily renewed, then it is not surprising that the seamounts and the rock of the floor are much younger than scientists had expected. They could not possibly be old. Nor is it surprising that much of the sediment seems to be missing. It is missing because it, too, has been carried away. Some has been carried down into the mantle. Some has gone into the making of mountains.

As they worked on the theory of ocean-floor spreading, certain scientists began to think of the earth's crust in a somewhat different way. They now

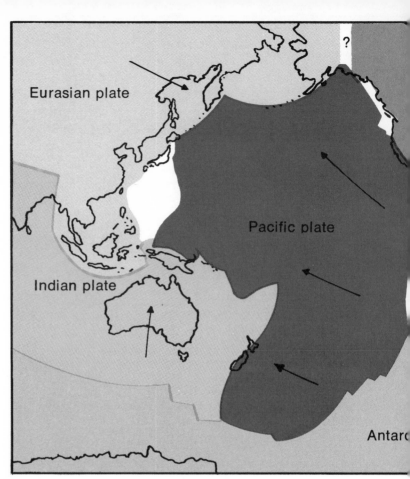

Eurasian plate

Pacific plate

Indian plate

Antar[c]

A number of earth scientists think of the earth's crust as divided into six major plates, five of them moving away from the African plate in the directions indicated.

think that it is divided into a number of rigid plates that float in the mantle. When they speak of ocean-floor spreading, they mean that huge plates of ocean floor are moving. They say that when two plates move away from each other, molten material from the mantle rises between them. It cools, solidifies, and joins the trailing edge of each plate. Meanwhile, the leading edge of each plate is pushing against some other plate. Where that happens, the leading edge may be forced downward into the earth; or it may buckle. Therefore material in the plate is created at the trailing edge and destroyed at the leading edge.

The theory of ocean-floor spreading goes far beyond solving mysteries of the ocean floors. It assumes

90

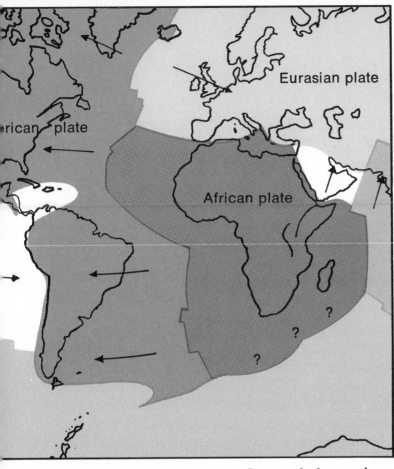

that, in addition to the sea floor, whole continents are moving, for they are embedded in the plates of the earth's crust.

Many earth scientists think that the Americas were once joined to Eurasia and Africa and that the continents were torn apart by an upwelling of molten material from the mantle. The place where they were once joined is now the Mid-Atlantic Ridge. As the continents were slowly carried away from each other, the gap between them became the Atlantic Ocean. There is reason to think that the continents are still slowly moving and that the Atlantic is still slowly widening. The Americas, for example, seem to be riding on a westward-moving plate.

There are no deep oceanic trenches off the eastern coast of South America. This fact fits well with the idea that the continent is moving westward. So does the fact that the eastern coast is not one of the active areas of the earth. It has no young mountains, no volcanoes, and no strong earthquakes.

Along the western coast the situation is very different. Here the westward-moving plate that carries the continent meets an eastward-moving plate of the Pacific floor. The details of what happens are not clear, but a number of earth scientists suppose that something like this occurs. The Pacific plate dives under the continent. Its plunge creates the deep trenches that parallel the west coast of South America. Where the edges of the two plates collide beneath the continent, they buckle—and the Andes crumple out of the crust. The mountains are made of rock from the continent and of rock and sediment from the ocean bottom. As the crumpling takes place, underlying rock melts and new volcanic material is added to the mountain chain.

An area where mountains are being forced up out of the crust is under great strain. Rock fractures and earthquakes take place. Rock melts and volcanoes erupt. And that is what seems to be happening along the west coast of South America. It is a region of huge young mountains, volcanic eruptions, and severe earthquakes.

Something similar seems to be taking place in various other parts of the Pacific. In that ocean there are chains of islands, such as Japan and the Philippines, that are known as island arcs. The island arcs

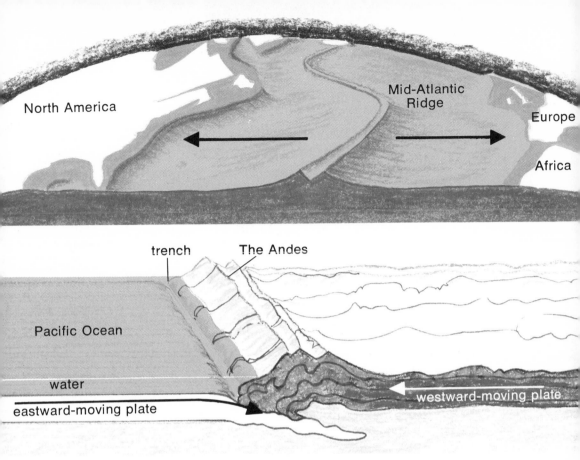

North America

Mid-Atlantic Ridge

Europe

Africa

trench   The Andes

Pacific Ocean

water

eastward-moving plate

westward-moving plate

are regions of young mountains, active volcanoes, and strong earthquakes. They are paralleled by deep oceanic trenches. It seems likely that in these regions the leading edges of two plates are colliding. Denser material is plunging downward, forming trenches, while less dense material is forced up into island arcs.

North America is apparently being carried westward on the same huge plate as South America. As is true with South America, there are no deep trenches paralleling the eastern coast, and the eastern part of North America has no young folded mountains, no active volcanoes, and few earthquakes. But along the western coast several things seem to be happening.

93

Many earth scientists think that the floor of the Northern Pacific is spreading in a northwesterly direction. One sinking place is marked by the deep trench that parallels the Aleutians, an island arc. The other sinking places are so far unknown, but the plate of ocean floor apparently thrusts its way under Alaska, accounting for Alaska's young mountains, strong earthquakes, and active volcanoes.

Farther south, at British Columbia, the mid-ocean ridge is close to the coast. A small plate that spreads eastward from the ridge may be crumpling against the coast. Still farther south, the plate and the ridge itself seem to have been overrun by the westward movement of the continent; this may account for the earthquakes and volcanic activity of the western United States. The ridge appears again in the Gulf of California. The gulf was formed long ago by the upwelling of the ridge, which tore Lower California away from the continent and turned it into a peninsula. If the ocean-floor spreading continues, Lower California will one day become an island.

The theory of ocean-floor spreading is new, and it has not been fully worked out. But it does seem to fit the facts and to solve many problems. To a growing number of earth scientists it is a most promising explanation of the forces that make this restless earth alive.

That alone, however, does not prove the theory is true. And so earth scientists have been looking for ways to test it.

There are places, for example, where the ridge-and-rift system climbs out of the water and can be

94

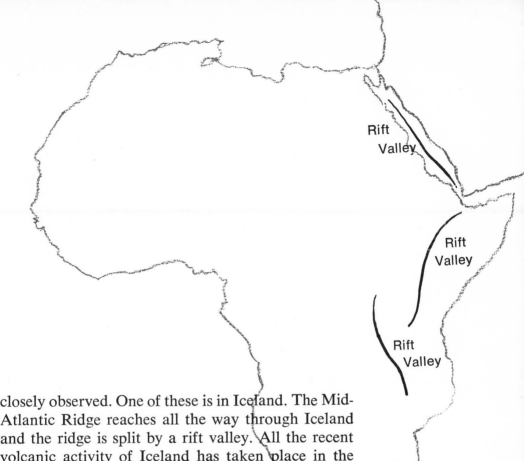

Rift
Valley

Rift
Valley

Rift
Valley

closely observed. One of these is in Iceland. The Mid-
Atlantic Ridge reaches all the way through Iceland
and the ridge is split by a rift valley. All the recent
volcanic activity of Iceland has taken place in the
rift valley. And measurements show that the rift is
very slowly widening. While this does not prove that
the ocean floor is spreading, it does show that the rift
results from tension, that forces within the ridge are
pulling it apart.

The rift can also be seen in eastern Africa, where
it has created the great Rift Valley. Here, earth
scientists think, the earth's crust is being pulled apart
and the breakup of a continent has begun. As with
Iceland, the evidence fits the theory and supports it.
But it does not prove the theory. What is happening
in Africa takes place so slowly that it cannot be
measured in human time.

Another piece of evidence has to do with the ages

of certain islands. Oceanographers had discovered that there were many smaller ridges lying beside the main mid-ocean ridge. Often the smaller ridges were at right angles to the main ridge. Peaks of the smaller ridges sometimes rose above the surface, forming islands such as the Azores, Bermuda, and the Hawaiian Islands. By dating the rocks of some of these islands, geologists discovered that the youngest islands were apparently those closest to the mid-ocean ridge and the oldest were apparently those farthest away. That is, the age of the islands seemed to increase with their distance from the mid-ocean ridge. It was as if islands were forming at or near the ridge and being slowly moved away from it.

If the ocean floor was spreading, that was just what would happen. At the same time, however, the islands were not proof that the floor was spreading. There might be a different explanation of their ages.

Real proof would lie in the age of the rock on the ocean floors. If the ocean floor was spreading, the age of the rock on every ocean floor should increase with the distance from the ridge. And the increase should be the same on both sides of the ridge.

The problem was to find a way of dating all the rock of the ocean floors. To do it by drilling for samples would be an almost impossibly big job. Was there, scientists wondered, some other way to date the rock? Not long ago, the answer turned out to be yes. Scientists studying rock magnetism discovered that there is a built-in calendar, or time scale, on the ocean floor. It has been created by changes in the earth's magnetic field.

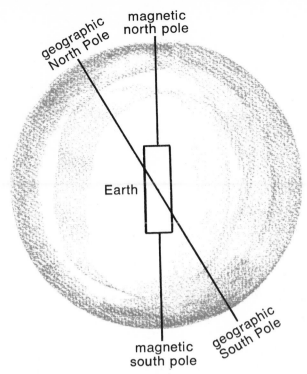

geographic North Pole

magnetic north pole

Earth

magnetic south pole

geographic South Pole

8   A Magnetic Time Scale

The earth is a giant magnet. Earth scientists today are almost certain that the earth is a kind of electromagnet, that its magnetic field is caused by electric currents in the earth's core. But in picturing the earth's magnetism, scientists find it useful to imagine that the earth contains a small but extremely powerful bar magnet.

This imaginary bar magnet lies at the earth's center. It does not quite line up with the earth's axis of rotation but is slightly tilted. A straight line drawn through the two poles of the magnet represents the earth's magnetic axis. The magnetic axis pierces the earth's surface at two places. These places are the earth's magnetic poles: the magnetic

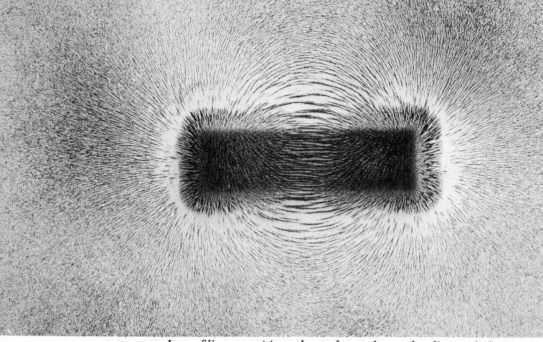

Iron filings position themselves along the lines of force, showing the magnetic field of a bar magnet.

north pole and the magnetic south pole. The magnetic poles are near, but not at, the geographic poles. (That is one reason why compass readings must be corrected. A compass needle points toward the magnetic north and not toward the true north of the geographic pole.)

Every bar magnet has invisible lines of magnetic force that arch from one pole to the other. The space where these lines of force are found around a magnet is called a magnetic field. The earth's magnetic field starts at the imaginary bar magnet and extends through the solid earth out into space.

This bar magnet is a helpful device, but it is only a fiction. No bar magnet could exist in the heat of the earth's core. Iron can neither be magnetized nor hold its magnetism at such high temperatures. To explain the earth's magnetic field, scientists have turned instead to the idea of electric currents in the

98

earth's core, for electric currents and magnetism are closely related.

No one knows exactly what magnetism is. But all magnetic fields are in some way caused by electric currents. If you run a current through a wire, a magnetic field forms around it. It is also true that a magnetic field can be used to produce an electric current in a continuous conductor; this is called an induced current.

Most earth scientists think that those facts contain the explanation of the earth's magnetism. They think that the magnetism originated in the outer core when the earth was very young. There churning molten metal created a small electric current. The current produced a small magnetic field. As molten metal moved through the field, electric currents were induced in it. These currents, in turn, gave the earth a magnetic field. The process continues to this day. Electric currents in the molten outer core create a magnetic field that spreads out from the core through the earth and into space.

Certain materials can be magnetized by a magnetic field. That is, if they are placed in a magnetic field, they become magnets themselves.

For example, an ordinary large steel sewing needle is not a magnet. But you can magnetize it, or make a magnet out of it, by stroking it with a bar magnet. By stroking it, you are placing the needle in a magnetic field. Start at the middle of the needle and stroke toward the point with one end of a bar magnet. Stroke this half of the needle about ten times in one direction only. Then turn the needle around. With the other end of the bar magnet stroke this half of the needle toward the eye. Do this about ten times, again only in one direction. The needle is now a magnet that can pick up pins, needles, or steel paperclips. It can also substitute for a compass needle.

The sewing needle becomes a magnet because it is made of steel. Steel, like iron and a few other materials, can be magnetized. The reason is that these materials are made up of tiny magnetic units called magnetic domains. Each domain may contain a cluster of millions of billions of atoms. The movement of electrons inside these atoms creates a tiny electric current. The current gives the domain its magnetism.

In an ordinary piece of iron or steel the domains face in all directions. Their effects cancel out, and the piece of metal is not a magnet. But if the piece of metal is placed in a strong magnetic field, the domains swing around in the direction of the field. When a great many domains have been lined up in one direction, the whole piece of iron or steel becomes a magnet.

As long as the domains are in line, the piece of metal remains a magnet. If they get out of line, it loses its magnetism. Heat is one thing that can destroy magnetism. If a steel magnet is heated, it loses its magnetism, because some of the domains get out of line. Heat can also prevent magnetism. Red-hot iron cannot be magnetized, because the domains do not stay in line.

What is true of pieces of iron and steel is also true

100

*Domains face in different directions in un-
magnetized material.*

In magnetized material, they line up.

of grains of iron and other magnetic minerals that occur in many of the earth's rocks. Under certain conditions they can be magnetized by the earth's magnetic field. Their domains line up and they become tiny magnets. That happens when the grains are present in molten rock that has cooled to a certain temperature.

When molten volcanic rock pours out of the earth, it is so hot that the iron in it cannot be magnetized. But when the minerals cool to a point where crystals start to form, the grains of iron are magnetized. The domains in each grain are lined up with the earth's magnetic field and are locked in place. Unless the rock is reheated, the grains keep that magnetism. And so they are a record of the direction of the earth's magnetic field at the time the rock became solid. To put it another way, the rock is full of tiny compass needles, all pointing to the magnetic north of the time when the rock hardened.

When these tiny compass needles are found in ancient rock, they serve as "fossil magnets." Study of fossil magnets has led to several interesting discoveries. One of them is that from time to time the earth's magnetic field reverses itself. That is, there have been times in the earth's history when the magnetic north pole has been near the geographic South Pole. If this were to happen now, the needle of every compass in the world would swing 180 degrees from north to south. Wherever molten rock was cooling and crystallizing, the magnetic domains in grains of iron would line up with the earth's magnetic field and point south.

101

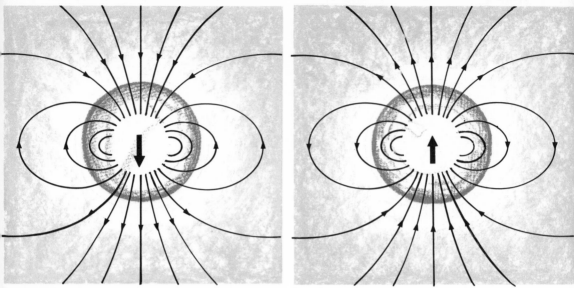

When the magnetic north pole lies near the geographic South Pole, the magnetic field is reversed.

The discovery of fossil magnets that pointed south was first made early in this century. The discovery suggested that the earth's magnetic field sometimes reversed itself, but no one paid much attention to the idea until a few years ago. Then a group of earth scientists decided to investigate it. They did this by analyzing and dating many samples of volcanic rock from several parts of the world.

For dating the rock the scientists chose potassium-40, which has a half-life of 1.3 billion years and decays into the gas called argon-40. They chose potassium-argon for two reasons. One is that potassium-40 occurs in almost all rock. The other is that argon-40 becomes trapped in the crystal structure of the rock. This means that it cannot start to collect until the volcanic rock has cooled to a point where crystals form. In most cases, the gas thus serves as an atomic clock that starts to run at exactly the time when magnetism is frozen into the rock.

By the end of their investigation, the scientists

were convinced that the earth's magnetic field does flip, or reverse itself. And by dating lavas they had started to work out a time scale for these changes. They dated periods when the field was normal, as it is now. They dated periods when the field was reversed, with the north magnetic pole near the geographic South Pole. For example:

Normal	from present	to 700,000 years ago
Reversed	from 700,000 years ago	to 850,000 years ago
Normal	from 850,000 years ago	to 950,000 years ago
Reversed	from 950,000 years ago	to 1.8 million years ago

After several years of work, scientists were able to draw up a very long time scale. If it is correct, then the earth's magnetic field has flipped 171 times in the last 76 million years. Some of the changes lasted only 30,000 years, while others lasted as long as 2 million years.

These studies were of great interest to many scientists, among them those who had been measuring the earth's magnetic field on the ocean floor.

The field's strength at the earth's surface can be measured with sensitive instruments called magnetometers. When scientists wish to measure the field at the ocean floor, they tow magnetometers behind ships or attach them to airplanes that fly over the areas under study.

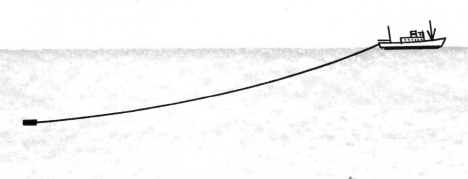

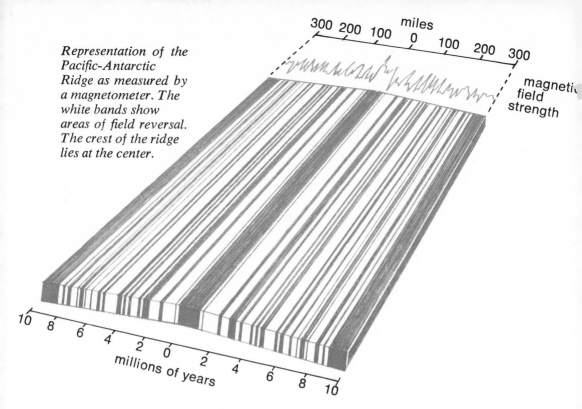

Representation of the Pacific-Antarctic Ridge as measured by a magnetometer. The white bands show areas of field reversal. The crest of the ridge lies at the center.

Measurements from the Atlantic showed a number of variations in the strength of the magnetic field. When the variations were mapped, they formed a striped pattern on the ocean floor. In one stripe, or band, the magnetism was stronger, in the next weaker, in the following band stronger, and so on. Each band was long and thin. Its width could be measured in tens of miles, but it might be hundreds or thousands of miles long. For the most part the bands ran parallel to the Mid-Atlantic Ridge.

Oceanographers thought that this odd magnetic pattern must have to do with the rock of the ocean floor. There was no reason to think that the magnetic field itself was producing the stripes. The most likely explanation was that the pattern was caused by rock magnetism, that the rock of the ocean floor was affecting measurements of the earth's magnetic

104

These magnetic stripes parallel the Juan de Fuca Ridge (between arrows). Tears, or fracture zones, at right angles to the ridge break the pattern of the stripes.

field. And this was to be expected if the ocean floor was spreading outward from the ridge.

For millions of years molten rock would have welled out of the ridge, hardened, and been carried away from the ridge. As the rock cooled, grains of iron in it would be magnetized. These tiny compass needles would point north if the earth's magnetic field was normal at the time the rock cooled. They would point south if the field was reversed. And so the rock would occur in bands of normal and reversed magnetism. A normal band would add to the strength of the earth's present magnetic field. A reversed band would subtract from it. Magnetic measurements would therefore show a striped pattern. Starting at the ridge, there should be a band of strong magnetism, followed by a weaker band, followed by a stronger band, and so on.

That was exactly what the magnetic measurements showed. And it was strong evidence that the ocean floor was indeed spreading.

There were signs that the floor had spread at different rates in different places along the ridge. Sometimes the stripes were broken by what seemed to be long tears, or fracture zones. Here large sections of the pattern had been moved sideways and might be hundreds of miles out of place. It was as if the ocean floor lay on a series of conveyor belts that were side by side but moving at different rates.

Earth scientists decided to test the theory of ocean-floor spreading still further. If the ocean floor was spreading, then the same striped pattern should ap-

105

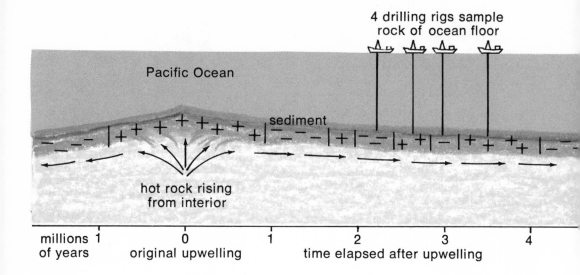

4 drilling rigs sample
rock of ocean floor

Pacific Ocean

sediment

hot rock rising
from interior

millions 1   0   1   2   3   4
of years   original upwelling   time elapsed after upwelling

Area in Pacific Ocean where the four rigs above drilled holes in parallel magnetic bands. White bands show reversed magnetic fields.

pear on every ocean floor. New studies showed that it did. On each side of the mid-ocean ridge there were long, thin stripes running parallel to the ridge. Moreover, the patterns on each side of the ridge were mirror images of each other. Like the patterns on the wings of a butterfly, they were the same but opposite.

It was possible to date the magnetic bands on the ocean floor. When the earth's magnetic field flips, the effects are worldwide. The change in magnetism affects cooling molten rock both on the ocean floor and on land. Oceanographers could therefore borrow the time scale developed by scientists studying fossil magnets on land.

By measuring and dating the bands, they could calculate the rate of spread. They found that the rate has varied. It has been faster in some periods than in

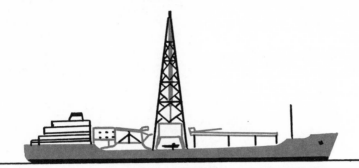

others. It may also vary in different parts of the
world. For example, at present the spreading is
greater in the Pacific than in the Atlantic. On each
side of the East Pacific Rise the ocean floor appears
to be spreading at a rate of two inches a year. At the
Reykjanes Ridge in the North Atlantic the spreading
is less than half an inch a year.

The Glomar Challenger *with its drilling rig*

Many earth scientists found these studies completely convincing. Oceanographers began to check
their findings by drilling a series of holes in the
floors of the Atlantic and Pacific and bringing up
samples of rock to analyze and date. But scientists
who had been studying the ocean floor and rock
magnetism no longer doubted what was happening.
The ocean floor was spreading.

The whole idea of ocean-floor spreading was new
and exciting and highly challenging to many scientists. Even so, it was only half the story of what was
happening, for if the ocean floors were moving, so
were the continents. By tracing the history of ocean-
floor spreading back some 120 million years, oceanographers might find themselves in a time when a
supercontinent was being torn apart, when the Atlantic Ocean was no more than a widening crack between the Americas and the Old World. The theory
of ocean-floor spreading has given new life to the
much older theory of drifting continents.

The Red Sea flows between Ethiopia (at left) and the Arabian Peninsula. Photograph by Gemini 11 from a distance of 390 miles shows neat fit of these two land masses, which are apparently drifting apart.

9   The Case for Continental Drift

Were the Americas once joined to Europe and Africa? The possibility first stirred men's minds several hundred years ago, as explorers mapped the Atlantic shores of the New World and the Old. These early maps brought to light something that has fascinated people ever since: the remarkable jigsaw-puzzle fit of South America and Africa. The eastern bulge of South America fills the hollow curve of the west coast of Africa, and the southern parts of the two continents fit neatly together. If North America is turned slightly, it fits into the puzzle, too. The western bulge of Africa fills the great hollow between Trinidad and Nova Scotia.

109

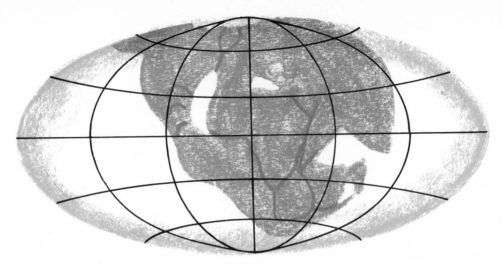

Wegener's supercontinent and how it drifted apart

The picture catches at the imagination, but it was not until the late 1800s that certain earth scientists began to wonder whether the continents had indeed once been joined. The question arose chiefly in the minds of geologists working in the Southern Hemisphere. They kept finding similar rock formations in the Old World and the New. By matching shapes and rock formations, an Austrian geologist named Eduard Suess was able to fit the lands of the Southern Hemisphere together. He named the big land mass Gondwanaland, after a province in India where he had found certain key rocks.

By the early 1900s a number of scientists had considered the idea that the continents had moved about, but the first to work out an overall theory was a German named Alfred Wegener. In 1912 he suggested that all the continents had once been joined in a single supercontinent, which he called Pangaea from the Greek meaning All-Earth. About 200 million years ago, he said, the supercontinent had broken up and the pieces had slowly drifted to where they are today.

Like other scientists of his time, Wegener knew that the continents float in the mantle and move up

110

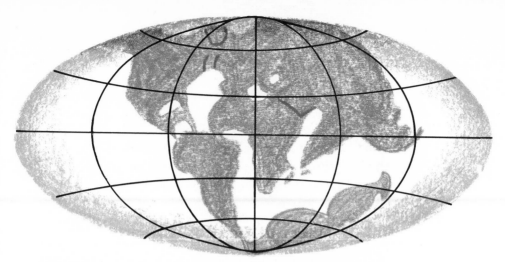

and down. In his day, as in ours, northern lands were slowly rising as ice from the last ice age melted. Wegener argued that if the continents could move up and down, they could also move sideways. He thought of the continents as plowing their way through the mantle as ships plow through the sea.

Wegener supported his theory with a number of findings, all of which suggested that the continents had moved.

He pointed out, for example, that coal is found all over the Northern Hemisphere. It is even found on the Arctic island of Spitzbergen. Yet coal forms from plants that grow in tropical forests, and so coal-bearing lands must once have had a tropical climate. It was also true that many warm parts of the Southern Hemisphere bore the marks of an ancient

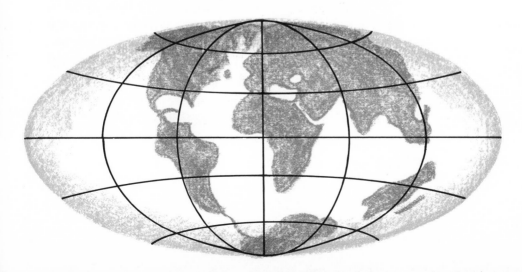

ice age. There was no way, Wegener said, for the Southern Hemisphere to have had an ice age while the Northern Hemisphere was basking in tropical warmth. On the earth, regions near the equator must always be warmer than regions near the poles.

Wegener thought that there was only one way to account for the coal-bearing lands of the north and the glacier-marked lands of the tropics. The continents must have moved.

He also pointed out an astonishing number of similar fossils and rock formations on both sides of the Atlantic. In fact, Wegener said, the rock records of South America and Africa matched so well that the two continents were like a torn sheet of newspaper—put the pieces together and you could read across the lines of print.

Wegener's theory stirred up a great discussion among earth scientists. No one could prove the theory was wrong, but few scientists supported him. Most thought that the rock and fossil records could be explained without drift. Even more important, no one could think of a force powerful enough to move whole continents.

The idea of continental drift has never really died out, however, for there are findings in several fields of science that are difficult to explain unless the continents have moved.

For one thing, there is the fossil record. A fossil is the remains of an animal or plant that lived in an ancient era. Fossils can be bones or shells. They can be footprints preserved in rock. They can be impressions in rock of plants or insects.

112

Mesosaurus—an early form of aquatic reptile—was about two feet long.

Fossil evidence shows that identical plants and animals once lived in places that are today hundreds or thousands of miles apart. For example, about 300 million years ago, big-leafed plants called *Glossopteris* became widespread. Their fossils have been found in South America, South Africa, Australia, India, and Antarctica. The fossil leaves from all these places are exactly alike. Many scientists think that these plants must first have developed on a single continent that later split up. They think it unlikely that identical plants could have developed in these far-flung places.

Fossils of a toothed reptile called *Mesosaurus* have been found in only two places: the east coast of Brazil and the west coast of South Africa. *Mesosaurus* lived in the water, but most scientists do not think this reptile could have crossed the South Atlantic.

Fossils also show that Antarctica was once a tropical or near-tropical land, a fact that is very difficult to explain if that continent has always been at the South Pole. The icy land has beds of coal. It

113

has fossils of *Glossopteris*. Pieces of fossilized wood show that a region within a short distance of the South Pole was once heavily forested. And not long ago a geologist found a fossil that is a very important clue to Antarctica's past. In rock that formed some 200 million years ago he found part of a jawbone from a long-vanished group of animals called labyrinthodonts. The labyrinthodonts were amphibians, animals that spend part of their lives on land and part in water. They were fresh-water amphibians, about the size of alligators, that are known to have lived in Africa and South America. Scientists think that, like today's fresh-water amphibians, these ancient ones could not live in salt water. So the discovery raises the question of how labyrinthodonts reached Antarctica, unless Antarctica was once part of a supercontinent.

The marks of ancient glaciers provide a different sort of clue to the past. During its history the earth has had several ice ages. An ice age begins when, for unknown reasons, there is a change in climate. In the cold parts of the world—in polar lands and far up lofty mountains—heavy snows fall. They fall and they pile up, for the summer sun cannot melt them all. The weight of new snows packs the old into ice. And then, as the weight keeps growing, the ice begins to flow. Creeping forward, great glaciers advance over the land.

The glaciers are mighty masses of ice with wall-like tongues, perhaps a mile high. Though they move very slowly, nothing can stop them. Forests crumple like matchsticks before them. Mountains and hills

114

*Glacier in the Chugach Mountains, Alaska. Melting ice forms
a stream at the leading edge.*

**This Alaskan glacier near Juneau dwarfs the cars and truck
parked on the opposite side of the water.**

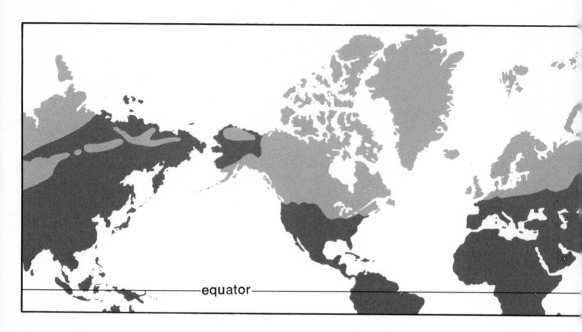

equator

In the last ice age, much of the Northern Hemisphere was covered by glaciers.

vanish under sheets of ice. The flowing ice carves and polishes the rocky faces of mountains. It gouges the land, picking up soil and boulders and carrying them along. Like a gigantic bulldozer, a glacier's tongue may push a huge pile of dirt and rock ahead of it.

Finally there is another change in climate, and the ice age ends. The ice melts. The glaciers draw back to the far places of the world, back to the polar lands and the mountaintops. Though the ice has gone, its marks are on the land. To those who can read them, the marks tell of the ice age. They tell what parts of the land were covered and in what direction the ice was moving.

116

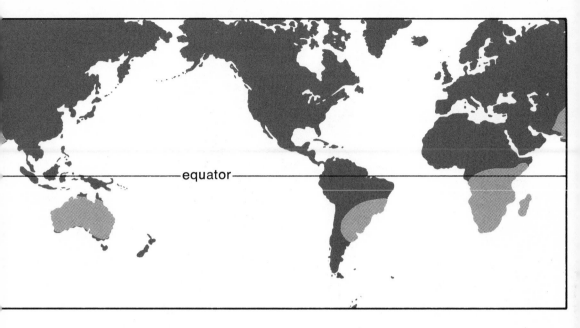

In an earlier ice age these areas, which are now near the equator, were covered with ice.

There are clear signs that one ice age took place 200 or 230 million years ago. It covered parts of South America, Africa, the Falkland Islands, India, and Australia. When these areas are marked on a map, scientists are faced with a number of puzzles. The glaciers of that ancient ice age spread across areas where there is no ice at all today. They covered areas that were untouched by glaciers during the last ice age. And the direction of flow indicates that some glaciers climbed out of the sea onto the land. Yet this is impossible. Glaciers are land ice, and they do not form in the sea.

One way to explain the marks of the glaciers is to suppose that the continents have moved since that

117

The way a computer fits the continents together. Strongest color indicates continental shelves. Land masses that overlap are shown in black; gaps are white.

ancient ice age took place. Many earth scientists think that the lands of the Southern Hemisphere must have been massed together at that time. They further think that some of the lands must have been much closer to the South Pole than they are today.

Still another piece of evidence comes from the study of fossil magnets. Comparing rocks of the same age from different continents, geologists have made an odd discovery. The tiny compass needles frozen into the rock of one continent line up with one another. But they do not line up with the fossil magnets of other continents. It is as if each continent had had its own north magnetic pole. Since that is impossible, scientists working in rock magnetism have turned to a different solution. They think that the continents have changed their relative positions since the time when the fossil magnets formed. If the continents have both drifted and swung around, the fossil magnets would now point in different directions.

The very first thing that made people wonder about drift, the jigsaw-puzzle fit of the continents, is still a strong argument in its favor. Modern scientists, however, have stopped trying to fit today's shorelines together. Instead, they are experimenting with fitting continental shelves. The shelves are part of the continents, and it is very likely that some 200 million years ago the shelves were dry land. At that time, a huge amount of the earth's water was locked up in ice that covered lands of the Southern Hemisphere, and ocean levels must have been much lower than they are now.

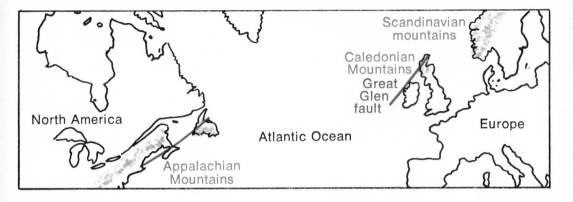

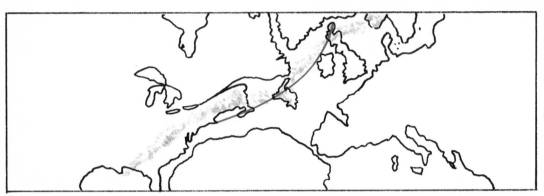

When the continents are fitted together, the Great Glen fault and the mountain chains form continuous lines with the faults and mountains in North America.

One of the most recent geographical matchings was done with the help of a computer. The result was a remarkable fit of the Americas with Africa and Europe. The continental shelves fit together and so do certain geographical features. There is, for example, a huge and ancient fault that cuts through Scotland along the Great Glen in the Caledonian Mountains. There is a series of faults in North America that seems to link up into one huge and ancient fault that runs from northern Newfoundland to Boston. When the continents are fitted together, these two ancient faults appear to be one. That is, one is an extension of the other. Mountains also match up.

120

The Appalachians run from Alabama to northern Newfoundland, where they end in the sea. When the continents are fitted together, they appear to be an extension of the Caledonian and Scandinavian mountains. All are old, worn mountains of the same age.

The same fitting together led to the discovery of an extraordinary matching of rock formations. In West Africa there are two clearly defined areas of rock. One, with rock that is 2 billion years old, runs through Ghana and the Ivory Coast and continues westward. The second, with rocks that are 600 million years old, runs through Dahomey and Nigeria

South America

Africa

121

and continues eastward. There is a sharp boundary between the two areas, and it ends in the ocean near Accra in Ghana.

Several scientists reasoned that if Brazil had been joined to Africa 600 million years ago, the same two rock zones should exist in Brazil. And the boundary should enter Brazil near the town of São Luis. They dated the rocks near São Luis and found that these fell into two age groups. The rocks to the west were 2 billion years old. The rocks to the east were 600 million years old. The match was perfect.

To many earth scientists such findings are overwhelming evidence that the Americas were once joined to Africa and Europe.

But the idea is by no means accepted by all earth scientists. It is strongly opposed by many geologists who have specialized in studies of land in the Northern Hemisphere. They believe that the continents and ocean basins formed as the molten earth cooled and that the continents have ever since remained frozen in place. The continents have been shaped and much changed by various forces, but they have remained in the places where they were formed. Over the years these geologists have questioned the evidence in favor of drift and argued against it. Some of their arguments have raised serious doubts about the evidence. Their strongest arguments, however, have concerned cause. What could cause a supercontinent to break up? What force could move whole continents over the face of the earth? No answer ever seemed entirely satisfactory. No answer really took care of the doubts and questions. No answer satisfied even the scientists who believed in drift.

That is, no answer did until very recently. Today earth scientists who believe in drift are convinced that the right answer has been found—and found on the ocean floors. The theory of drift has also gained many new supporters among scientists working in rock magnetism and oceanography. If the theory of ocean-floor spreading is correct, as they think it is, then the continents have drifted and are still drifting today.

These scientists think that several hundred million years ago the continents were joined together. Some think that the continents formed one big land mass, which they call Pangaea. Others think that there were two big land masses, Laurasia and Gondwana-land. Laurasia was made up of North America, Europe, and Asia. Gondwanaland was made up of South America, Africa, Antarctica, Australia, New Zealand, India, and Madagascar.

A laser reflector was placed on the moon by the Apollo 11 *astronauts. When laser beams sent from different continents bounce back to earth, their coordinated measurements may prove whether or not the continents are drifting apart.*

Starting some 200 to 300 million years ago, up-wellings of hot material began to tear the continents apart and to move them away from one another.

First, North America began a slow swing away from Europe, rotating on a point that was probably in Alaska.

Somewhat later, perhaps 150 to 200 million years ago, South America and Africa began to pull apart. South America was carried westward. Africa rotated clockwise, pushing northward into Europe and Asia. In time the Mediterranean became a small, closed sea. Southern Europe crumpled, and the Alps were thrust up.

Meanwhile in the Southern Hemisphere a big rift opened up as India, Madagascar, Australia, New Zealand, and Antarctica were torn away from the tip of Africa. As millions and millions of years passed, New Zealand and Australia separated from Antarctica. They drifted north and east. Antarctica was carried toward the South Pole. Madagascar became

an island off the east coast of Africa. India drifted northward until it collided with Asia. The collision crumpled the earth's crust and forced up the Himalayas. Where the continents had split apart, the Indian Ocean formed.

By 100 million years ago, the major separations of the continents had taken place, with the continents moving toward their present positions. And as the New World and the Old were moved apart, the Atlantic Ocean slowly opened up. It grew from a broad and salty "river" to an ocean that covers nearly 32 million square miles.

This picture of the earth's changing face is based on the mapping of magnetic patterns on the ocean floors. Scientists have traced the direction of materials that welled out of the ridge and calculated the time that the spreading has taken. Working from this information, they have been able to trace the "footprints" of the continents, to trace their paths backward through time.

Some earth scientists are looking back even further in time. They think it unlikely that there has been only one period of continental drift during the earth's long history. It is much more likely that the processes at work today have always been in action. These scientists think that the continents must have split many times in the past, forming new oceans, and must also have collided a number of times, welding together new land masses.

Mountains offer one clue to earlier periods of drift. If the earth's young folded mountains have formed as drift crumpled them out of the crust, then it seems likely that older folded mountains were formed in the same way. They must mark what were once the edges of continents, bordering an ocean. A number of earth scientists think, for example, that sediments now in the Caledonian and Appalachian mountains were laid down in an ocean that closed long before the Atlantic opened. They feel sure that the Atlantic did not exist 150 million years ago. Since the mountains are much older that that, their sediments must have come from some now-closed ocean, at a time when geography was very different from what it is today.

Studies of rock magnetism and the ocean floor have opened up vast new areas of research in the earth sciences. They have made the earth sciences one of the most exciting and fast-changing fields to work in, as old ideas give way and new ideas are put to the test. Today earth scientists seem to be on the verge of answering some of the most basic questions about the earth, of understanding why the earth has continents and mountains, volcanoes and earthquakes. They are on the verge of understanding the forces that shape and change the earth, that keep it alive within, and that make it a planet where many kinds of life are possible.

The key seems to lie in the mid-ocean ridge and the molten rock that wells out of it. And so the small island of Surtsey may be something much more than a new volcanic island. It may be a dramatic sign of the forces that move continents, build mountains, cause earthquakes, and make volcanoes erupt.

Surtsey

Author's note

In recent years many scientists have made important discoveries and advances in the areas of earth science described in this book. While it was impossible to credit these researchers by name in the text, I should like to acknowledge here the names of those whose work and reports loomed large in my research for this book. They are: P. M. S. Blackett, Edward Bullard, S. W. Carey, Allan Cox, G. Brent Dalrymple, Robert S. Dietz, Richard R. Doell, J. P. Eaton, Maurice Ewing, Bruce C. Heezen, J. R. Heirtzler, Harry H. Hess, Patrick M. Hurley, Bryan Isacks, Harold Jeffreys, Gerard P. Kuiper, Xavier Le Pichon, D. H. Matthews, Henry W. Menard, W. Jason Morgan, K. J. Murata, Jack Oliver, S. K. Runcorn, Lynn R. Sykes, Marie Tharp, Sigurdur Thorarinsson, F. J. Vine, J. Tuzo Wilson.

Biographies

PATRICIA LAUBER, formerly editor-in-chief of a young people's science magazine and Chief Editor, Science and Mathematics, for a leading children's encyclopedia, is the author of some 40 books, many concerning science. Her Random House books include *Who Discovered America?* and titles in four series. A graduate of Wellesley College, she now lives in New York City.

JOHN POLGREEN has illustrated many science books, including several for the Random House Look-It-Up series. He is an active member of the Association of Lunar and Planetary Observation of Variable Star Observers. In collaboration with his wife, Cathleen, who is also an enthusiastic amateur astronomer, he wrote and illustrated *The Earth in Space*. The Polgreens live in Dobbs Ferry, New York.

Index

Page numbers in **bold face** are illustrations.